Contents

Contents

Name _____

Be a Problem Solver!

Many problems have more than one solution. For each of the following problems, write down at least two different ways to solve it!

Problem #1: One of the wheels on your bicycle breaks.

_____

_____

Problem #2: You're having a hard time understanding your math homework.

_____

_____

Problem #3: Your parents won't give you money to buy the game you want.

_____

_____

Name _____

Problem Solvers

	Who is the main character? What problem does he or she have?	What are some benefits that result from solving the problem?
My Name Is María Isabel		
Marven of the Great North Woods		
The Last Dragon		
Sing to the Stars		

Name _____

Vocabulary Scramble

Unscramble the vocabulary words and write them on the lines.

Vocabulary

attentively
disappointed
misunderstanding
nervously
troublesome

ddppiisantoe __ __ __ __ ◯ __ __ ◯ __ __ __ __

Hint: means "having unsatisfied hopes or wishes"

youvernsl __ __ ◯ __ __ __ __ __ __

Hint: means "with worry or concern"

aeeiytttnvl ◯ __ __ __ __ __ __ __ __ __ __

Hint: means "alertly or with great attention"

lbreetoosum ◯ __ __ __ __ __ __ ◯ __ __ __ __

Hint: means "causing trouble or difficulty"

uddsstmiinnnerag

__ __ __ ◯ __ __ __ ◯ __ __ __ __ __ __ __ __

Hint: means "a failure to understand"

Unscramble the circled letters to answer the question.

What does the chorus do before a winter concert?

__ __ w __ __ __ __ __ __ .

Name _____

Prediction Chart

Details about María Isabel	
María Isabel at School	**What María Isabel Likes**
_____	_____
_____	_____
_____	_____
_____	_____
María Isabel's Life at Home	**What María Isabel Wishes**
_____	_____
_____	_____
_____	_____
_____	_____
_____	_____

What will happen in next year's school pageant?

_____

_____

_____

4   Theme 4: **Problem Solvers**

Name _____

A Diary Entry

What if María Isabel kept a diary? Help her finish this page in her diary by completing the sentences.

Because there are two other girls named María in my class, my teacher

doesn't call me _____.

_____ are the only three

kids who don't have parts in the play.

The others don't mind, but I feel _____.

My only comfort is _____.

My problems don't seem so bad compared with _____.

When I rode the bus home today, I sang _____

_____ and I felt a little better.

I cannot tell _____ that I am not in
the pageant, because they will be so disappointed.

I'm so glad I wrote an essay on _____
because it led me to get a part in the pageant.

Name _____

What Might Happen?

**Read this story and then answer the questions
on the following page.**

My Mean Brother

It was the first day of the new school year, and my first
day of fifth grade. This meant going to a new school, the same
one as my older brother, Kevin. He was in seventh grade.

Kevin had been trying to scare me all summer about Mrs. D.,
my new teacher. He'd say things such as, "Look out, Bryan,
Mean Mrs. D. doesn't like kids. She once sent me to the
principal's office for sneezing! She doesn't let you erase your
mistakes. And she even does surprise fingernail checks to make
sure they are neat and clean!" I laughed at Kevin, wondering if
he was telling the truth.

Being really nervous about the first day of school, I couldn't
believe my luck when I missed the bus. Kevin made me go
back in the house to get his lunch, but when I did, the bus
drove by and Dad told me Kevin already took his lunch!

My dad took me to school that day, telling me not to let
Kevin bother me. But I was bothered by the fact that we were
late! All I could think about was what Mean Mrs. D. was
going to do to me!

When we arrived, I ran up and down the hallway, searching
for Mrs. D.'s classroom. I guess I was making a lot of noise because
Mrs. D. opened her door as I skidded to a stop in front of her.

"Oh, you must be Bryan," she said. "I was worried about you.
Glad you made it. Why don't you get a drink of water, and then
come to class."

Name _____

What Might Happen? continued

Answer each of the following questions with a prediction about what will happen and the details from the story that support that prediction.

1. What do you think Bryan will do when he and Kevin return home from school?

   Prediction: _____

   _____

   _____

   Supporting Details: _____

   _____

   _____

2. What kind of student do you think Bryan will be in Mrs. D.'s class?

   Prediction: _____

   _____

   Supporting Details: _____

   _____

3. What do you think Bryan would be like as an older brother?

   Prediction: _____

   _____

   Supporting Details: _____

   _____

   _____

Name _____

Is It Poss*ible?*

**Write T if the statement is true. Write F if the statement is false.
If you are unsure of a word's meaning, use a dictionary.**

_____ 1. Chocolate cake is <u>edible</u>.

_____ 2. It is <u>sensible</u> to play with matches.

_____ 3. It is easy to see things that are <u>invisible</u>.

_____ 4. A <u>collapsible</u> tent is one that you can fold up when you
are not using it.

_____ 5. A <u>convertible</u> car can be changed so that it has no top.

_____ 6. If something is <u>permissible</u>, you are allowed to do it.

_____ 7. If something is <u>audible</u>, you can smell it.

_____ 8. Rubber is a <u>flexible</u> material.

_____ 9. A <u>reversible</u> jacket always looks the same.

_____ 10. It is <u>responsible</u> to forget your homework at home.

Name _____

The /k/, /ng/, and /kw/ Sounds

Remember these spelling patterns for the /k/, /ng/, and /kw/ sounds:

/k/	k, ck, c	(shar**k**, atta**ck**, publi**c**)
/ng/	(before *k*) *n*	(si**n**k)
/kw/	*qu*	(**qu**estion)

► In the starred words *ache* and *stomach*, /k/ is spelled *ch*.

Write each Spelling Word under the correct heading.
Circle the words with the /ng/ sound.

1. shark
2. attack
3. risk
4. public
5. sink
6. question
7. electric
8. jacket
9. blank
10. ache*
11. crooked
12. drink
13. topic
14. track
15. blanket
16. struck
17. mistake
18. junk
19. squirrel
20. stomach*

/k/ Spelled *ck*

_____
_____

/k/ Spelled *k* or *c*

_____   _____
_____   _____
_____   _____
_____   _____

Other Spellings for /k/

_____   _____

/kw/

_____   _____

Theme 4: **Problem Solvers**   9

Name _____

Spelling Spree

Daily News Write the Spelling Word that best completes each sentence.

Swimmer Bumped by Unidentified Object

Vacationers were upset by a report that a

(1) _____ had been spotted in the water.

Fred Finn was (2) _____ in the leg by "a huge

white fish." A family that had just spread out their

(3) _____ on the sand nearby claimed the fish

was indeed a "great white." Police Chief Ann Summer

wasn't convinced this was an actual (4) _____.

"Unless there's a real (5) _____ of someone

getting bitten, the beach will remain open," she declared.

Mr. Finn escaped with an (6) _____ in his leg.

He said, "I'm just glad I didn't end up as a meal in that

monster's (7) _____!"

Write a Spelling Word by adding the beginning of the first word to the end of the second word.

8. topcoat + music

9. size + think

10. jackpot + bonnet

11. crooning + wicked

12. job + trunk

13. election + metric

14. squirm + barrel

15. blue + tank

8. _____

9. _____

10. _____

11. _____

12. _____

13. _____

14. _____

15. _____

Spelling Words

1. shark
2. attack
3. risk
4. public
5. sink
6. question
7. electric
8. jacket
9. blank
10. ache*
11. crooked
12. drink
13. topic
14. track
15. blanket
16. struck
17. mistake
18. junk
19. squirrel
20. stomach*

Name _____

Proofreading and Writing

Proofreading Circle the five misspelled Spelling Words in this billboard advertisement. Then write each word correctly.

There's no kwestion about it!

Potato latkes are great! They're crispy and tasty and easy to make. It doesn't matter whether you're celebrating Hanukkah or just want to enjoy a fantastic treat. Serve them with a tall drinck and a mound of applesauce. Make no misstake! An admiring publick will sing your praises. Be careful cooking, though. There's always a risk of getting splattered with hot oil, and remember to keep trak of hot cookware at all times.

1. _____

2. _____

3. _____

4. _____

5. _____

Spelling Words

1. shark
2. attack
3. risk
4. public
5. sink
6. question
7. electric
8. jacket
9. blank
10. ache*
11. crooked
12. drink
13. topic
14. track
15. blanket
16. struck
17. mistake
18. junk
19. squirrel
20. stomach*

Write a Letter How does your family celebrate a special day? Do you exchange presents? Do you cook special food or sing special songs? Do friends and relatives come to visit?

On a separate sheet of paper, write a letter to tell a friend what happens at your house on the special day. Use Spelling Words from the list.

Theme 4: **Problem Solvers**   11

Name _____

Will You Find the Word in the Entry?

Read each sentence. In the space write *yes* if you think the underlined word would be part of a dictionary entry for the base word. Write *no* if you think it would not be part of the base word entry. Then circle the base words for *yes* answers in the word find box.

1. Everything at school <u>revolved</u> around plans for the
   Winter Pageant. _____

2. The class <u>talked</u> about Hanukkah and other holidays. _____

3. María Isabel's problems were <u>smaller</u> than Wilbur's. _____

4. Wilbur was in danger of <u>becoming</u> the holiday dinner. _____

5. She felt herself getting <u>sadder</u> each day. _____

6. What was <u>waiting</u> for her in the next few days? _____

7. The teacher asked, "What is your <u>greatest</u> wish? _____

8. The boy <u>dropped</u> his crutch only once during rehearsal. _____

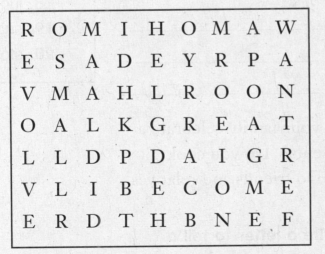

R	O	M	I	H	O	M	A	W
E	S	A	D	E	Y	R	P	A
V	M	A	H	L	R	O	O	N
O	A	L	K	G	R	E	A	T
L	L	D	P	D	A	I	G	R
V	L	I	B	E	C	O	M	E
E	R	D	T	H	B	N	E	F

Name _____

Completing with *be*

Complete each sentence by filling in the blank with the form of *be* that goes with the subject. Use the correct form for the tense named in parentheses.

1. This photo _____ a picture of my mother and father. (present)

2. We _____ in Santo Domingo for the holidays. (past)

3. My family _____ there two years ago. (past)

4. Those two melodies _____ very familiar to me. (present)

5. Many of the songs _____ from other countries. (present)

6. Three students _____ not in the play. (past)

7. What _____ your favorite story about animals? (present)

8. Wilbur _____ the main character in María Isabel's favorite story. (present)

9. What _____ your wish for the new year? (past)

10. What _____ María Isabel's full name? (present)

Name _____

To be in the Past or the Present

**Complete the sentences by writing a form of the verb
be. In the first four sentences, use the past. In the last
four sentences, use the present.**

1. María Isabel _____ troubled about Wilbur.

2. María Isabel _____ unhappy about not being in the
   pageant.

3. Her parents _____ there two years ago.

4. _____ María Isabel nervous in front of
   the class?

5. María Isabel _____ happy about leading the song.

6. The butterfly barrettes _____ a present from
   María Isabel's father.

7. The Hanukkah song _____ María Isabel's favorite.

8. María Isabel wrote, "Most of all, I _____ proud
   of my name."

**Now make up two sentences of your own, telling
something about María Isabel and her experiences at school.
Use a different tense of *be* in each sentence.**

_____

_____

_____

_____

Name _____

Writing with the Verb *be*

Using Forms of the Verb *be* Good writers are careful to use
tense forms of *be* that match the subjects. Read the paragraph
below. Rewrite the paragraph, correcting tense forms of *be* so that
they match the subject of the sentence.

  I think that holiday songs is my favorite kind of music. These
songs be very tuneful. Our school program will have a lot of them.
The first song on the program are for guitar and voice. It were
once a lullaby. You and I know the music by heart. We is in the
chorus.

_____

_____

_____

_____

_____

_____

_____

_____

_____

_____

_____

_____

Name _____

Writing an Opinion

Use this page to plan how you will write a paragraph expressing your *opinion* in a convincing way. Use facts or reasons to support your opinion. Number your facts or reasons in the order you will present them. Finally, restate your opinion.

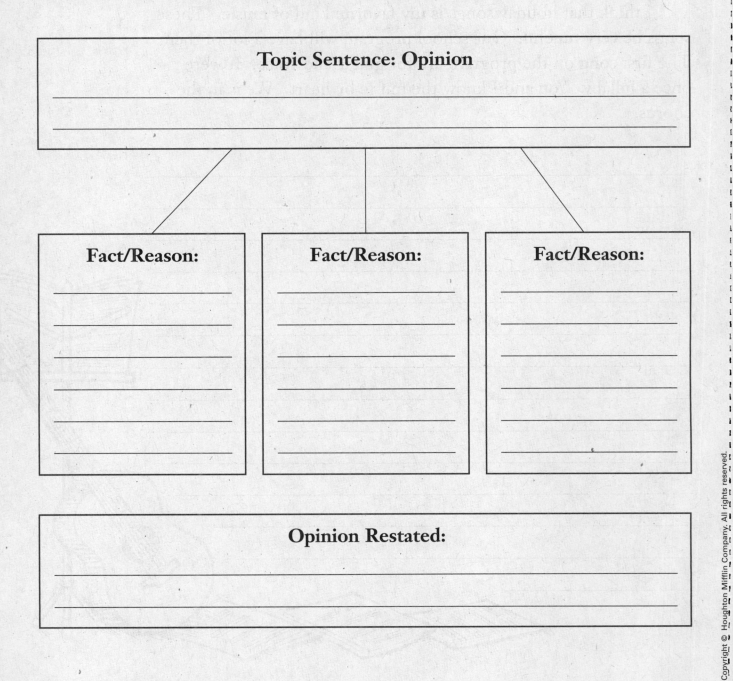

Topic Sentence: Opinion

_____

_____

Fact/Reason:

_____

_____

_____

_____

_____

Fact/Reason:

_____

_____

_____

_____

_____

Fact/Reason:

_____

_____

_____

_____

_____

Opinion Restated:

_____

_____

Name _____

Using Commas with Introductory Phrases

A phrase is a small group of words that acts as a part of speech. A phrase at the beginning of a sentence is called an **introductory phrase**. Good writers use introductory phrases to vary sentence length and make sentences interesting. Introductory phrases should be set off with a comma.

At first, María Isabel Salazar López did not know she was being addressed.

Read the following sentences. If the sentence has an introductory phrase, write the sentence on the lines below and add a comma to set off the introductory phrase.

1. After helping with the dishes she finished her homework.

   _____

   _____

2. In time María Isabel told her parents about her problem.

   _____

   _____

3. The teacher agreed to the request made by María Isabel's parents.

   _____

   _____

4. Pleased to be called by her full name María Isabel agreed to sing her favorite song.

   _____

   _____

5. María Isabel's mother and father were there to hear her sing.

   _____

Name _____

Revising Your Persuasive Essay

Reread your persuasive essay. Put a checkmark in the box for each sentence that describes your paper. Use this page to help you revise.

Rings the Bell

☐ I state my goal clearly in the introduction.

☐ I support my goal with strong reasons. Each reason is supported by facts and examples.

☐ My paper is organized in paragraphs. My conclusion is strong.

☐ I used many persuasive words. The writing shows how I feel.

☐ Sentences flow smoothly. There are almost no mistakes.

Getting Stronger

☐ I do not state my goal clearly in the introduction.

☐ I need more reasons. There could be more facts and examples.

☐ Some paragraphs are disorganized. My conclusion is weak.

☐ I need more persuasive words. I don't always show how I feel.

☐ Some sentences are choppy. There are some mistakes.

Try Harder

☐ The goal is not clear. The introduction is missing.

☐ There are almost no reasons. There are no facts or examples.

☐ My paper has only one paragraph. I did not write a conclusion.

☐ I used no persuasive words. I don't seem to care about my goal.

☐ Most sentences are choppy. There are many mistakes.

18   Theme 4: **Problem Solvers**

Subject-Verb Agreement

► Add *-s* or *-es* to most verbs to show the present tense if the subject is singular.

That frog jump**s** high.   He watch**es** frogs all day.

► Do not add *-s* or *-es* to most verbs to show the present tense if the subject is plural or the word *I*.

Frogs swim in our pond.   I watch frogs all day.

Complete each sentence. Circle the correct form of each verb.

1. Frogs (is/are) amphibians.

2. An amphibian (has/have) wet skin.

3. Amphibians (live/lives) both on land and in the water.

4. Toads (is/are) actually a type of frog.

5. Toads (has/have) dry skin and a stumpy body.

6. Both frogs and toads (breathe/breathes) through their skin.

7. Scientists (worry/worries) about frogs.

8. One scientist (blame/blames) ozone loss for the problem.

9. Gaps in the ozone layer (let/lets) dangerous UV rays through.

10. The UV rays (damage/damages) frogs.

Spelling Words

Words Often Misspelled Look for familiar spelling patterns to help you remember how to spell the Spelling Words on this page. Think carefully about the parts that you find hard to spell in each word.

Write the missing letters in the Spelling Words below.

1. ___ ure
2. h ___ ___ ___
3. ___ ___ ew
4. m ___ ___ ___ t
5. pre ___ ___ y
6. rea ___ ___ y
7. v ___ ___ y
8. ___ ___ ere

9. lit ___ ___ ___
10. unt ___ ___
11. int ___
12. o ___ ___
13. s ___ ___ d
14. ___ ___ r
15. let ___ ___ ___ r

Spelling Words

1. sure
2. here
3. knew
4. might
5. pretty
6. really
7. very
8. where
9. little
10. until
11. into
12. off
13. said
14. our
15. letter

Study List On a separate piece of paper, write each Spelling Word. Check your spelling against the words on the list.

Name _____

Spelling Spree

Contrast Clues The second part of each clue contrasts with the first part. Write a Spelling Word for each clue.

1. not there, but _____

2. not ugly, but _____

3. not on, but _____

4. not a phone call, but a _____

5. not big, but _____

6. not your, but _____

7. not out of, but _____

Word Magic Replace or add one letter in each word below to make a Spelling Word. Write it on the line.

8. untie _____

9. rally (add one letter) _____

10. knee _____

11. right _____

12. sand _____

13. vary _____

14. pure _____

15. here _____

Spelling Words

1. sure
2. here
3. knew
4. might
5. pretty
6. really
7. very
8. where
9. little
10. until
11. into
12. off
13. said
14. our
15. letter

Theme 4: **Problem Solvers** 21

Name _____

Proofreading and Writing

Proofreading Circle the five misspelled Spelling Words in this dialogue. Then write each word correctly.

Pam: Well, they said that was the last bus untill 6:15.

Zack: So I guess we're stuck hear for another three hours.

Pam: I guess you mite say that.

Zack: I'm sorry—I was shur I'd have time to run and get a snack. Who new that the bus would leave on time?

Pam: There's *got* to be some other way of getting home.

Spelling Words

1. sure
2. here
3. knew
4. might
5. pretty
6. really
7. very
8. where
9. little
10. until
11. into
12. off
13. said
14. our
15. letter

1. _____

2. _____

3. _____

4. _____

5. _____

Stating the Problem What are some problems you would like to see someone try to solve? On a separate piece of paper, write four sentences that describe problems you think need solving. Use Spelling Words from the list.

Bus stop schedule

Name _____

Words in the Woods

> ### Vocabulary
>
> bunkhouse   cords (of wood)   immense   landscape
>
> lumberjacks   snowshoes   timber   woodsman

The woods are full of words from the vocabulary list. Write each word above the tree trunk that shows its meaning.

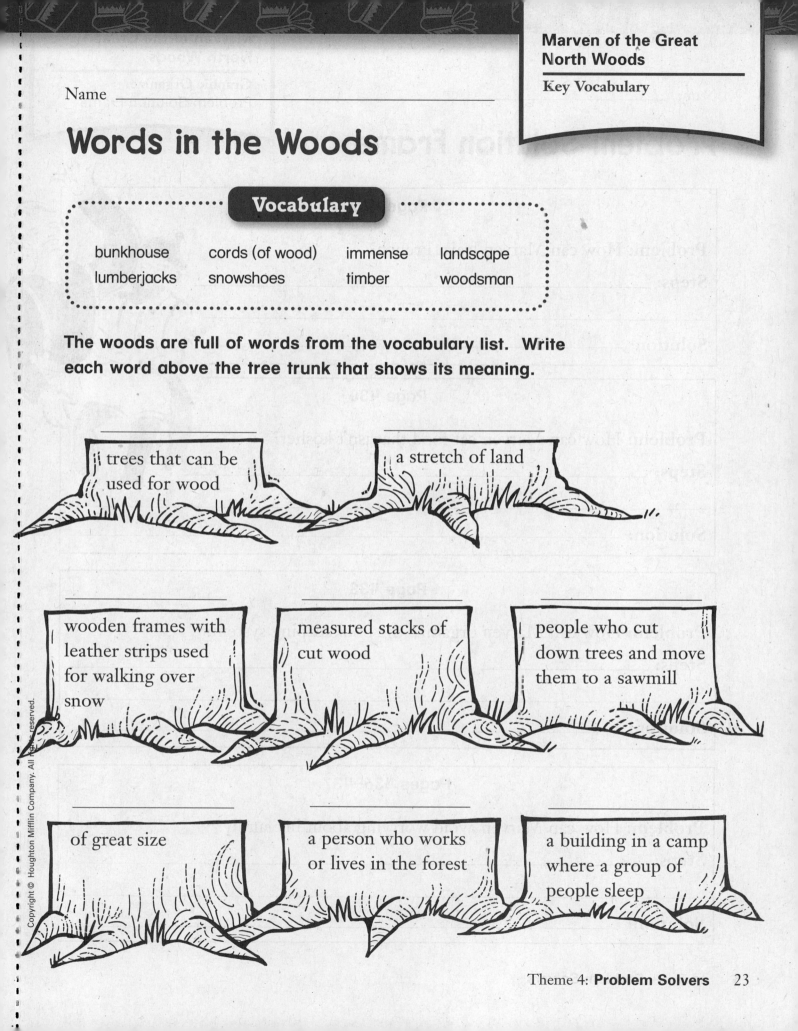

_____   _____

trees that can be used for wood   a stretch of land

_____   _____   _____

wooden frames with leather strips used for walking over snow   measured stacks of cut wood   people who cut down trees and move them to a sawmill

_____   _____   _____

of great size   a person who works or lives in the forest   a building in a camp where a group of people sleep

Name _____

Problem-Solution Frame

Page 419

Problem: How can Marven learn French?

Steps: _____
_____

Solution: _____

Page 430

Problem: How can Marven eat food that isn't kosher?

Steps: _____
_____

Solution: _____

Page 433

Problem: How can Marven organize the bookkeeping system?

Steps: _____
_____

Solution: _____

Pages 436–437

Problem: How can Marven avoid worrying about his family?

Steps: _____
_____

Solution: _____

Name _____

Write a Letter

Suppose Marven wrote a letter to his aunt and uncle. Help him complete the letter.

Dear Aunt Ghisa and Uncle Moishe,

    I know it was a good idea for me to leave the city to make sure I didn't get _____, but I miss all of you.

    Here at the logging camp, Mr. Murray asked me to _____ since I have a good head for numbers.

    One of the scariest things I had to do my first morning at camp was to _____.

    Now I have lots of fun with _____, a huge lumberjack, because we are friends.

    No matter how much fun I have in the great north woods, I will be happy in spring when I can _____, _____.

      Your nephew,
      Marven

Name _____

A Cold Adventure

Read the story. Then complete the chart on the following page.

Race to the Pole

In the far north, a group of men struggled against icy wind. It was 60 degrees below zero. It was so cold that frostbite could occur in minutes. The explorers wore thick fur parkas, gloves, and boots to protect themselves against the cold. Robert Peary and Matthew Henson would not give up. They wanted to be the first explorers to reach the North Pole.

In 1909, no one had ever been to the North Pole. People believed it was somewhere in the Arctic Ocean at the very top of the world. That far north it is light for six months and dark for six months. The explorers could not cross the ice in the dark. But if they waited too long to leave, the summer sun would melt the ice before they could cross it coming back.

The Arctic Ocean this far north also contains great chunks of ice. The men had to cut through the ice to move on. They carried their supplies on sledges, long sleds pulled by teams of dogs. The dogs had to be fed, too, which meant the men had to carry a lot of food.

The pull of the moon's gravity and the movement of Earth often crack the ice in the Arctic. This creates lanes of water called leads, which can split open at any time, plunging the explorers into the freezing water. So the team must always be prepared to get out of the water and change clothes quickly. If they did not get into dry clothes, they could freeze to death in minutes.

Peary and Henson had tried to reach the North Pole twice before. Both times they had been beaten by the freezing winds, huge blocks of ice, and starvation. Could they make it this time? They would not have another chance.

Name _____

A Cold Adventure continued

Problem	Solution
The extreme cold could cause frostbite.	
In the Arctic, it is light for six months and dark for six months.	
The men need help carrying their supplies.	
The moon's gravity and Earth's movement cause lanes of water in the ice to open up.	

If you were exploring a cold and icy place like the North Pole, what do you think would be the greatest problem you would face? Why? How would you solve it?

_____

_____

_____

_____

Theme 4: **Problem Solvers**   27

Name _____

Prefix Precision

Answer the questions.

1. Why might a **misprinted** book need to be **reprinted**?

_____

_____

2. Why is it an **excellent** idea to recycle?

_____

_____

3. Why should you try to **respell** a word that you have **misspelled**?

_____

_____

4. Why is it important to **reread** the directions during an **exam**?

_____

_____

5. Why should you **retrace** your steps when you **misplace** something?

_____

_____

Write the word in dark type above next to its meaning.

put in the wrong place   _____

outstanding   _____

printed again   _____

read again   _____

Name _____

Final /ē/

When you hear the final /ē/ sound in a two-syllable word, think of the spelling patterns *y* and *ey*.

beauty   honey

► In the starred word *movie*, the final /ē/ sound is spelled *ie*.

Write each Spelling Word under its spelling of final /ē/.

y	*ey*
_____	_____
_____	_____
_____	_____
_____	_____
_____	_____
_____	**Another Spelling**
_____	_____
_____	
_____	

Spelling Words

1. beauty
2. ugly
3. lazy
4. marry
5. ready
6. sorry
7. empty
8. honey
9. valley
10. movie*
11. duty
12. hungry
13. lonely
14. alley
15. body
16. twenty
17. turkey
18. hockey
19. fifty
20. monkey

Name _____

Spelling Spree

Word Search Circle the 15 Spelling Words in the puzzle. Then write them on the lines below.

```
L R E E A S H O C K E Y T H E
A C L A S P W S T T R I P T M
Z F I S H H U T H U L E E H P
Y O V E U K T U E S S M A R T
E A E Y N A F R Y L H O N E Y
T H S U G H H K I M O V E E S
S H Y R R O S E E A P I X E L
F I F T Y L E Y A Y B E T A N
U P V S H Y U L H M S W E E T
M A T I E U G L Y O U E N Y W
A L I M Y S L O A N B N O S E
R R A L A K E T W K I T T E N
R B O D Y Y L O N E L Y I V T
Y N Q U E E S T A Y A L L E Y
```

Spelling Words

1. beauty
2. ugly
3. lazy
4. marry
5. ready
6. sorry
7. empty
8. honey
9. valley
10. movie*
11. duty
12. hungry
13. lonely
14. alley
15. body
16. twenty
17. turkey
18. hockey
19. fifty
20. monkey

1. _____   9. _____

2. _____   10. _____

3. _____   11. _____

4. _____   12. _____

5. _____   13. _____

6. _____   14. _____

7. _____   15. _____

8. _____

Name _____

Proofreading and Writing

Proofreading Circle the five misspelled Spelling Words
in this poem. Then write each word correctly.

Marven's Adventure

His father said, "My son, go forth."

So ten-year-old Marven headed north.

Met in a vally by a stranger

Far from the city, out of danger.

He took a break from his daily dutie,

Skied in search of woodland beuty.

Though the lumberjack life was steady,

He missed his family and he was readey

To ski home over the springtime snow.

And his friends were sory to see him go.

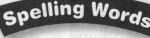

<table>
<tr><td>Spelling Words</td></tr>
</table>

Spelling Words

1. beauty
2. ugly
3. lazy
4. marry
5. ready
6. sorry
7. empty
8. honey
9. valley
10. movie*
11. duty
12. hungry
13. lonely
14. alley
15. body
16. twenty
17. turkey
18. hockey
19. fifty
20. monkey

1. _____   4. _____

2. _____   5. _____

3. _____

✏ **Write a Journal Entry** Pick your favorite
incident or picture from *Marven of the Great North Woods.*

**On a separate sheet of paper, write a journal entry that
describes what happened in the scene from Marven's
point of view. Use Spelling Words from the list.**

Name _____

All in the Word Family

In each box, read the clues and add endings to the underlined word to make words that fit the word family. Remember, an ending sometimes changes the spelling of the base word. The first word family is written for you.

t o w e r
two or more: t o w e r s
very tall: t o w e r i n g
in the past: t o w e r e d

---

f i d d l e

two or more: ___ ___ ___ ___ ___ ___ ___

person who plays a fiddle: ___ ___ ___ ___ ___ ___ ___

playing a fiddle: ___ ___ ___ ___ ___ ___ ___

played in the past: ___ ___ ___ ___ ___ ___ ___

---

t h i c k

more thick: ___ ___ ___ ___ ___ ___ ___

most thick: ___ ___ ___ ___ ___ ___ ___ ___

in a thick way: ___ ___ ___ ___ ___ ___ ___

---

f r e e z e

turning to ice: ___ ___ ___ ___ ___ ___ ___

a very cold place for food: ___ ___ ___ ___ ___ ___ ___

becomes ice: ___ ___ ___ ___ ___ ___ ___

Challenge Use the base word "camp" or "wild" and write clues for other words in the same family. Swap puzzles with a classmate.

Name _____

Irregular Completion

**Complete each sentence by writing the correct past tense form
of the verb named in parentheses.**

1. All the jacks have _____ snowshoes every day
   this winter. (wear)

2. The jack _____ the axe directly at the tree.
   (throw)

3. Marven's family _____ him to the train station.
   (take)

4. The train _____ to a full stop at Bemidji. (come)

5. Marven had _____ a new part of his life now.
   (begin)

6. Marven's father had _____ him skis for his sixth
   birthday. (give)

7. Marven's skis never _____ on his way from the
   station. (break)

8. Marven _____ latkes and knishes with him.
   (bring)

9. The days have _____ much shorter now. (grow)

10. Marven never _____ snow could stay white
    so long. (know)

Name _____

Verbs in a Letter

Write a letter to the author, Kathryn Lasky, to tell her why you enjoyed *Marven in the Great North Woods*. Use as least five of the verbs on the verb tree in your letter. Vary the verb tenses. A sample has been done for you.

Dear Ms. Lasky,

When I began to read your story about Marven at the lumber camp, I couldn't stop. I knew Marven would come to enjoy life in the north woods. I even brought the story home to show my parents. Thanks for writing such a good story. You have given me lots of interesting information about what it was like to grow up in the early 1900s.

give
wear
know
take
begin
come
break
throw
bring
grow

_____

_____

_____

_____

_____

_____

_____

Name _____

Using Irregular Verbs

Using the Correct Verb Form Read the first draft of the report on one day in Marven's life at the logging camp. On the lines below, rewrite the report, replacing any incorrect forms of irregular verbs with correct forms.

Marven had bring his skis along. One Friday, Marven put the skis on and taked off on the sled paths into the woods. He wear his heavy coat. Everything growed still and white. When he come to a frozen lake, he stopped. He know the scenery would be beautiful. He heard a growl. He begun to tremble. Was it a bear? Had a branch broke off? It give him quite a scare. Luckily, the noise had came from his friend Jean Louis.

_____

_____

_____

_____

_____

_____

Name _____

How to Take Notes

**Use this page to *take notes* on a winter activity. Research a
sport or hobby that interests you, or take notes on the article
about snowshoeing on pages 446–449 of your anthology.**

Research Question:
_____
_____

Main idea 1: _____

supporting detail: _____

supporting detail: _____

supporting detail: _____

Main idea 2: _____

supporting detail: _____

supporting detail: _____

supporting detail: _____

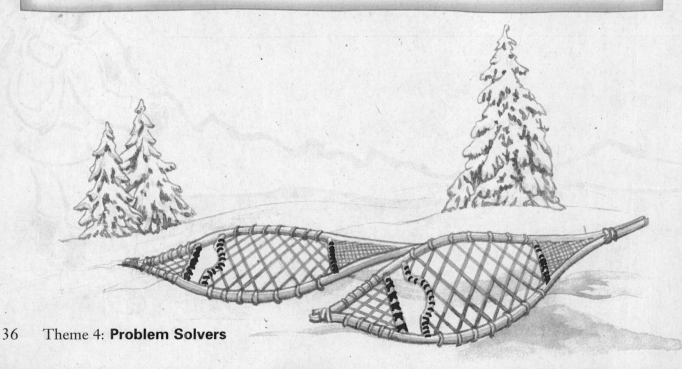

Name _____

Choosing What's Important

When writers take notes, they list main ideas and the important details that support the main ideas. To check whether a detail supports the main idea, reread the main idea. Ask: *Is this detail about the main idea?*

> **Main idea:** Use safety when snowshoeing.
> **supporting detail:** Go with a partner.
> **supporting detail:** Tell an adult where you are going.
> **supporting detail:** ~~snowshoes are 6,000 years old~~ *This detail is not about snowshoe safety.*

Read the following sets of notes. Use this proofreading mark ∂ **to delete the details that do not support the main idea.**

1. **Main idea:** Some mammals are well-adapted to life in the arctic regions.

   detail: Musk oxen and reindeer have large feet that allow them to walk on snow.

   detail: Lemmings, arctic fox, and gray wolves grow white winter coats.

   detail: Some kinds of whales are endangered worldwide.

2. **Main idea:** Some animals hibernate during the winter.

   detail: Bears and bats hibernate in caves.

   detail: Certain fish are found only in tropical waters.

   detail: Animals fatten up to hibernate.

Name _____

Scrambled Dragons

Unscramble the letters to make a word from the vocabulary list. Then solve the riddle.

gheoma __ __ __ __ __ __
$\quad\quad\quad\;$ 1
Hint: means "honor or respect"

lessac __ __ __ __ __ __
$\quad\quad\quad\quad$ 2
Hint: means "small, thin, flat parts that cover a reptile"

densak __ __ __ __ __ __
$\quad\quad\quad\quad\quad$ 3
Hint: means "moved like a snake"

ecefir __ __ __ __ __ __
$\quad\;$ 4
Hint: means "wild and mean"

crachearts __ __ __ __ __ __ __ __ __ __
$\quad\quad\quad\;\;$ 5 $\quad\quad\quad\quad\quad\quad\quad\quad\quad$ 6
Hint: means "marks or signs used in writing"

gniemet __ __ __ __ __ __ __
$\quad\quad\quad\;$ 7 $\quad\quad\quad\quad$ 8
Hint: means "to be full or crowded"

sterc __ __ __ __ __
$\quad\quad\;\;$ 9
Hint: means "something that grows out of an animal's head"

Write each numbered letter in the space with the same number to solve the riddle.

What does a dragon's breath feel like?

__ __ __ __ __ __ __ __ __ __
5　1　7 　2　6 　4　8　9　3

Name _____

Conclusions Chart

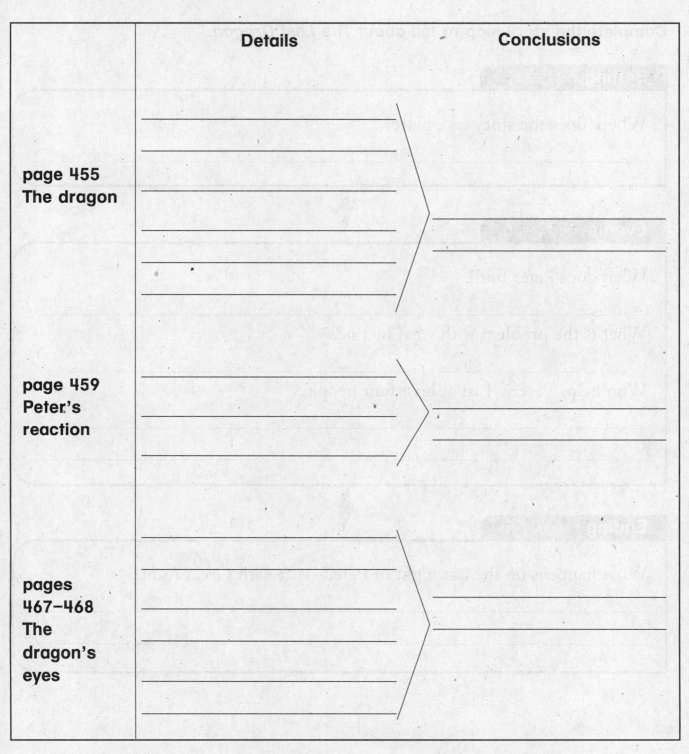

	Details	Conclusions
page 455 **The dragon**		
page 459 **Peter's** **reaction**		
pages **467–468** **The** **dragon's** **eyes**		

Name _____

Peter's Adventure

Complete the story map to tell about *The Last Dragon*.

Setting

Where does the story take place?

_____

Events

What does Peter find?

_____

What is the problem with what he finds?

_____

Who helps Peter? List at least four people.

_____

_____

Ending

What happens on the last night of Peter's visit with Great Aunt?

_____

_____

Name _____

A Snapshot of America

Read the article. Then read the statements on the next page. Decide if the statement is *true, false,* or if *not enough information* is given to draw a conclusion.

United States Population to Double

Washington, DC — By the year 2100, there will be twice as many Americans as there are today. Imagine twice as many cars on the highways. Imagine twice as many people in line at the supermarket. Can our nation handle the change?

Today about 275 million people live in the United States. According to the Census Bureau, by 2100 that number will be about 571 million. That would make our population density (people per area) a bit over 160 people per square mile. In comparison, the density of Germany today is over 400 people per square mile. It's a good thing that our country is large and vast.

Today there are around 65,000 people age 100 or older. In 2100, there may be 5 million. The elderly will make up one-fifth of our population. The median age (the age at which half the population is older and half younger) will rise by 2100 to over 40, compared to around 36 today.

The Hispanic population of the United States is expected to triple in the next 50 years. The Asian and Pacific Islander population will more than triple. Today, non-Hispanic white people make up about three-quarters of the population. Although that group will grow, too, by 2050, they will make up only about one-half of the total.

Name _____

A Snapshot of America continued

1. The Hispanic population in the United States is expected to double in the next 50 years.

   true   false   not enough information

2. The population density of Germany is greater than the population density of the United States.

   true   false   not enough information

3. Germany has a larger population than the United States has.

   true   false   not enough information

4. There are more Asian Americans than Hispanic Americans in the United States today.

   true   false   not enough information

5. In the year 2100, there will be more people in the United States over 100 years old than today.

   true   false   not enough information

6. Doubling the amount of cars will cause terrible gridlock.

   true   false   not enough information

7. By the year 2050, our population will be around 571 million.

   true   false   not enough information

8. The United States is vaster than Germany.

   true   false   not enough information

Name _____

Complete Prefix Control

Write two words from the box that together match each description. Use each word only once. Use a dictionary if you need help.

Example:

No one "exactly expected" how the dragon would look when finished.

In other words, no one **precisely predicted** how it would look.

commercial	concert	congratulations	preowned
committee	concise	constant	prerecorded
companion	concrete	construction	preserved
completely	condition	consumer	preteen
computer	confused	prehistoric	preventable

1. steady friend: _____

2. mixed-up group: _____

3. advertisement taped earlier: _____

4. buyer between the ages of 9 and 12:

_____

5. totally saved from an earlier time:

_____

6. used machine that runs programs:

_____

7. very old musical performance:

_____

8. brief words to express joy for someone's good luck:

_____

Name _____

Final /j/ and /s/

Remember these spelling patterns for the final /j/, /ĭj/, and /s/ sounds:

/j/ in a one-syllable word   *dge, ge*   (bri**dge**, stran**ge**)

/ĭj/ in a word of more than one syllable   *age*   (vill**age**)

/s/   *ce*   (en**ce**)

Remember that in words with a short vowel sound, final /j/ is spelled *dge*. In words with a long vowel sound, final /j/ is spelled *ge*.

Write each Spelling Word under the correct heading.

Spelling Words

1. village
2. cottage
3. bridge
4. fence
5. strange
6. chance
7. twice
8. cage
9. change
10. carriage
11. glance
12. ridge
13. manage
14. damage
15. since
16. marriage
17. edge
18. lodge
19. cabbage
20. dodge

/j/ in One-Syllable Words

_____

_____

_____

_____

_____

_____

_____

/ĭj/ in Two-Syllable Words

_____

_____

_____

_____

_____

_____

Final /s/ Spelled *ce*

_____

_____

_____

_____

_____

Name _____

Spelling Spree

Rhyming Pairs Complete each sentence by writing a pair of rhyming Spelling Words.

1–2. I had to duck and _____ snowboarders on my way to the ski _____.

3–4. The bride and groom rode off in a horse-drawn _____ to begin their _____.

5–6. I know this outfit looks a little _____, so I think I'll go back home and _____.

7–8. We must cross the _____ to get to the _____ on the other side of the river.

1. _____   5. _____

2. _____   6. _____

3. _____   7. _____

4. _____   8. _____

Quick Pick Write the Spelling Word that best matches the meaning of each word or group of words below.

Example: courtroom official   *judge*

9. animal carrier _____

10. vegetable _____

11. barrier around a garden _____

12. small town _____

13. small house _____

14. quick look _____

15. rim or border _____

Spelling Words

1. village
2. cottage
3. bridge
4. fence
5. strange
6. chance
7. twice
8. cage
9. change
10. carriage
11. glance
12. ridge
13. manage
14. damage
15. since
16. marriage
17. edge
18. lodge
19. cabbage
20. dodge

Name _____

Proofreading and Writing

Proofreading Circle the five misspelled Spelling Words in this ad. Then write each word correctly.

HELP WANTED

Experts Needed to Repair Dragon

At first glanse, he might not look like much. All this Chinese dragon needs, though, is tender loving care to repair a little damidge. If you can manige to spare some time to help, please ask for Peter at the noodle factory. In return for sewing, painting, frame repair, and blessings, I promise to run errands and do small jobs (sins I don't have any money for payment). Don't think twice. All the dragon needs is a chanse!

1. village
2. cottage
3. bridge
4. fence
5. strange
6. chance
7. twice
8. cage
9. change
10. carriage
11. glance
12. ridge
13. manage
14. damage
15. since
16. marriage
17. edge
18. lodge
19. cabbage
20. dodge

1. _____   4. _____

2. _____   5. _____

3. _____

Write a Thank-You Note Peter had help from a tailor, his great-aunt and her friends, a kite maker, a painter, and others. Choose one of the people who worked on the dragon and write that person a thank-you note that Peter might have written.

On a separate sheet of paper, write your note. Be sure to include the task the person performed and why the person's help was important. Use Spelling Words from the list.

Name _____

Add the Correct Suffix

Rewrite each sentence below, replacing the words in italics with one word. Make the new word by adding the suffix *-ful, -less*, or *-ly* to the underlined word. Use a dictionary if you need help remembering the meanings of the suffixes.

1. Great Aunt thought the old dragon was *without <u>hope</u>.*

   Great Aunt thought the old dragon was _____.

2. Great Aunt's *<u>full</u> of cheer* friends repaired the dragon's crest.

   Great Aunt's _____ friends repaired
   the dragon's crest.

3. Peter waited *in a <u>patient</u> way* for Mr. Pang to repair the dragon's body.

   Peter waited _____ for Mr. Pang to repair
   the dragon's body.

4. *With respect to <u>luck</u>,* Dr. Fong located eyes for the dragon.

   _____, Dr. Fong located eyes for the dragon.

Add *two* suffixes to the underlined word in each sentence below.

5. The dragon moved *in a manner without <u>effort</u>* on silken legs.

   The dragon moved _____ on silken legs.

6. Peter and his friends restored the dragon *in a way full of <u>beauty</u>.*

   Peter and his friends restored the dragon _____.

Name _____

Being Specific with Adjectives

Complete each sentence with the adjective from the box that fits best. Use each adjective only once. Underline the noun each adjective modifies. Write whether the adjective tells *what kind* or *how many*.

| two | tasty | loud | big | new |

1. Its mouth opened with a _____ sound.

_____

2. Fixing the dragon will be a _____ job.

_____

3. Miss Tam made _____ dumplings

_____

4. Peter did _____ things for Miss Rose.

_____

5. The kite shop was not far from the _____

restaurant. _____

Complete each sentence by choosing the correct article in parentheses. Then write your choice in the blank.

6. Peter noticed _____ severed tail. (an, the)

7. Miss Rose had _____ idea. (a, an)

Name _____

Dragon Menu

The pictures below show what foods might have been served at Peter's farewell dinner at the Golden Palace Restaurant. Write a caption for each picture, describing the food shown and how it tastes. Use adjectives to tell what kind and how many. Color the pictures to show what the foods look like and to help you describe them.

Won-ton Soup

_____

_____

_____

Noodles

_____

_____

_____

Peppery Shrimp

_____

_____

_____

Vegetables

_____

_____

_____

On a separate sheet of paper, write a description of something else you would like to see on the menu.

Name _____

Expanding with Adjectives

Good writers add interest and detail to their sentences by including adjectives that tell what kind and how many. Read the sentences below. Rewrite each sentence using specific adjectives that tell what kind or how many.

1. The crest on the dragon's head was _____ and _____.

_____

2. Peter didn't like Great Aunt's _____,_____ apartment.

_____

3. Peter was carrying a sack of _____, _____ crabs.

_____

4. The _____ jaw could move easily now.

_____

5. Miss Rose sewed _____, _____ scales on the tail.

_____

6. The _____ streets of Chinatown were filled with people.

_____

50   Theme 4: **Problem Solvers**

Name _____

Writing a Comparison/Contrast Composition

Use this page to plan your *comparison/contrast composition.*
Fill in the graphic organizer with details about how two places,
activities, or books are alike and different. Then, on a separate
sheet of paper, write a comparison/contrast composition.
When you have finished your composition, exchange papers
with a partner.

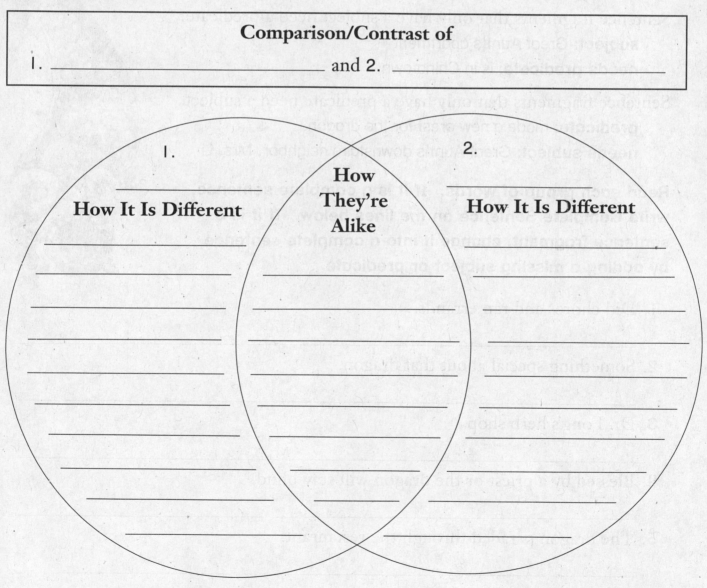

Comparison/Contrast of

1. _____ and 2. _____

1.

How It Is Different

How
They're
Alike

2.

How It Is Different

Name _____

Correcting Sentence Fragments

Writers know that **sentence fragments** can be used for any note-taking graphic organizer. Good writers also know to use complete sentences when writing paragraphs, essays, or reports. Complete sentences have subjects and predicates.

          subject   predicate
The English teacher / suggested showing the dragon to a kite maker.

Sentence fragments that only have a subject need a predicate.
    subject: Great Aunt's apartment
    needs predicate: is in Chinatown.

Sentence fragments that only have a predicate need a subject.
    predicate: made a new crest for the dragon.
    needs subject: Great Aunt's downstairs neighbor, Mrs. Li

Read each group of words. If it is a complete sentence, write Complete Sentence on the lines below. If it is a sentence fragment, change it into a complete sentence by adding a missing subject or predicate.

1. Did chores and ran errands.

  _____

2. Something special about that dragon.

  _____

3. Dr. Fong's herb shop.

  _____

4. Blessed by a priest or the dragon will stay blind.

  _____

5. The dragon paraded through the restaurant.

  _____

Name _____

Musical Meanings

Fill in the blanks with words from the vocabulary list to complete the news article.

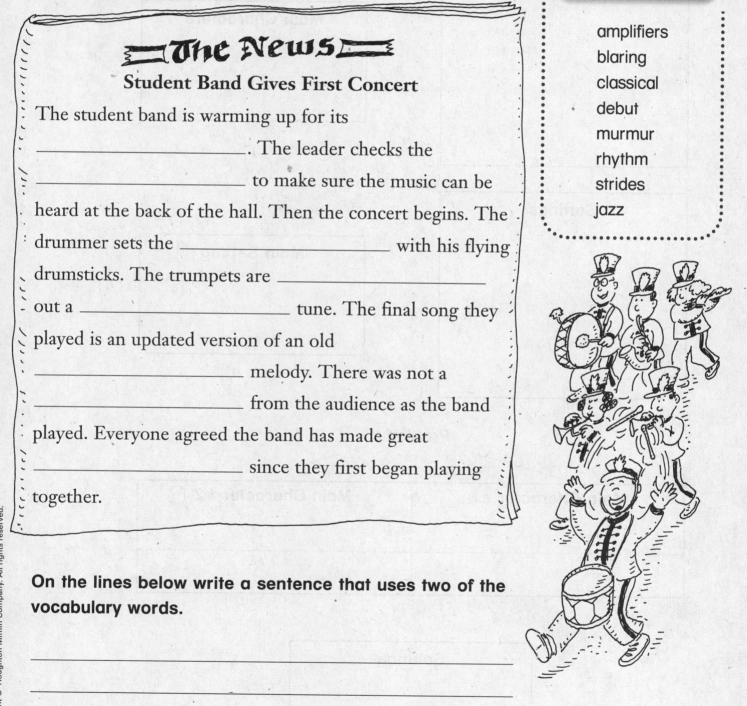

≡The News≡

Student Band Gives First Concert

The student band is warming up for its

_____. The leader checks the

_____ to make sure the music can be

heard at the back of the hall. Then the concert begins. The

drummer sets the _____ with his flying

drumsticks. The trumpets are _____

out a _____ tune. The final song they

played is an updated version of an old

_____ melody. There was not a

_____ from the audience as the band

played. Everyone agreed the band has made great

_____ since they first began playing

together.

Vocabulary

amplifiers
blaring
classical
debut
murmur
rhythm
strides
jazz

On the lines below write a sentence that uses two of the vocabulary words.

_____

_____

_____

Name _____

Story Structure Map

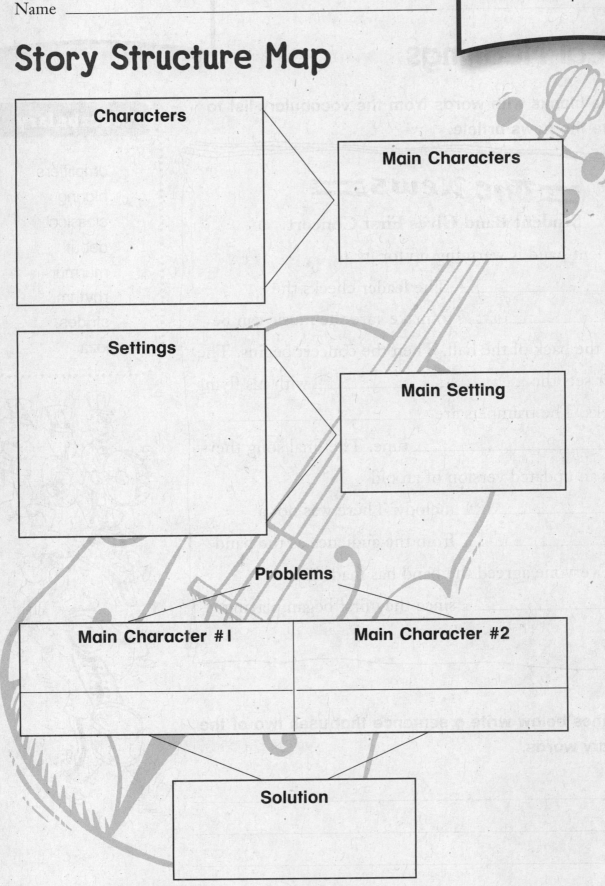

Characters

Main Characters

Settings

Main Setting

Problems

Main Character #1	Main Character #2

Solution

Name _____

Hear the Music

Complete each sentence to tell about *Sing to the Stars*.

1. Mr. Washington always knew that Ephram was coming because

    _____

    _____

2. When a rapper on the corner yelled to Ephram to get himself
    an electric guitar, Ephram

    _____

    _____

3. Mr. Washington stopped playing the piano when

    _____

    _____

4. Ephram said that he did not think he would play at the benefit
    concert because

    _____

    _____

5. The title of this story, *Sing to the Stars*, refers to

    _____

    _____

    _____

What Did You Say?

Read the story. Then complete the following page.

The Talking Yam

Once upon a time, a long time ago, not far from the city of Accra, a farmer went to dig some yams from his garden. While he was digging, one of the yams said to him, "Go away and leave me alone!" The farmer turned and looked at the cow in amazement. "Did you say something?"

The cow didn't answer, but the dog said, "The yam spoke to you. The yam says leave him alone."

The man became angry, so he kicked a stone. The stone yelled, "Hey, cut that out!" Frightened, the man ran to the village. On the way, he met a fisherman carrying a large fish. "What's your hurry?" the fisherman asked.

"My yam is talking to me! My dog is talking to me! The rock is talking to me!" screamed the farmer.

"So what's the fuss?" the fish answered. "Besides," the fishing pole added, "you shouldn't kick rocks." The farmer jumped, yelled, and went running to the king.

"My yam is talking to me! My dog is talking to me! The rock is talking to me!" screamed the farmer. "Then a fish talked to me and a fishing pole, too!"

The king listened to the farmer. Finally, he said, "This is a wild story. Go back to your work before I punish you for disturbing the peace." The farmer went away and the king shook his head. "What a silly story. Stories like this upset all the people."

"You're right," answered his throne. "Imagine, a talking yam!"

Name _____

What Did You Say? continued

Complete the chart for the story "The Talking Yam."

Main Character
_____

Setting
_____
_____

Farmer's Problem
_____

Beginning
_____
_____

Middle
_____
_____

End
_____
_____

Solution
_____
_____

Name _____

Syllable Sort

Pair up the syllables in the box to make words, then write the word that matches each clue and draw a line between the syllables.

1. a tooth doctor _____

2. a tool for hitting nails _____

3. a windy snowstorm _____

4. a marriage ceremony _____

5. the opposite of before _____

6. a hat used to protect the head _____

7. A cricket is a kind of _____

8. a person who has great skill _____

9. Six and nine are both _____

10. having no mistakes _____

wed	fect	hel	mer	ding	den	in	per	zard	tist
sect	bers	ham	ter	af	num	pert	bliz	met	ex

Name _____

VCCV Pattern

Knowing how to divide a word into syllables can help you spell it. Remember these rules for dividing two-syllable words with the VCCV pattern:

► Divide most VCCV words between the consonants, whether the consonants are different or the same.

► Divide a VCCV word before the consonants if those consonants form a cluster.

► Divide a VCCV word after the consonants if those consonants spell one sound.

VC | CV	**pic | ture, at | tend**
V | CCV	**a | fraid**
VCC | V	**oth | er**

Write each Spelling Word under the heading that shows where its syllables divide. Draw a line between its syllables.

VC | CV

_____   _____

_____

_____

_____

_____

_____   ### V | CCV

_____

_____   _____

_____   ### VCC | V

_____

_____

_____

Spelling Words

1. bottom
2. picture
3. other
4. attend
5. capture
6. common
7. danger
8. afraid
9. borrow
10. office
11. arrow
12. suppose
13. escape
14. whether
15. pillow
16. dinner
17. thirty
18. degree
19. allow
20. corner

Name _____

Spelling Spree

Write the Spelling Word in each word below.

1. officer _____

2. uncommon _____

3. supposed _____

4. bottomless _____

5. swallow _____

6. borrower _____

7. pillowcase _____

Write the Spelling Word that answers each riddle.

8. You might find me inside a frame. Who am I?

9. I'm speeding cars and thin ice. Who am I?

10. Along with breakfast and lunch, I'm a winner. Who am I?

11. I have a point, and I'm very narrow. Who am I?

12. I'm smaller than forty and bigger than twenty. Who am I?

13. If I'm not one thing, I'm the _____.

14. I'm hot or cold, high or low. Who am I?

8. _____   12. _____

9. _____   13. _____

10. _____   14. _____

11. _____

Name _____

Proofreading and Writing

Proofreading Circle the six misspelled Spelling Words in this neighborhood flyer. Then write each word correctly.

Concert After Dark Series

You're invited to atend a concert in the park
every Saturday in August!

Ninety-degree temperatures got you down? Enjoy a
concert and ekscape the summer heat. Come one, come all,
wether young or old. Don't be afriad to leave work early.
Invite your boss or bring a friend. Take the opportunity to
capshur the sounds of summer to remember all winter long.

Concerts are held right around the korner in Davis Park.

1. bottom
2. picture
3. other
4. attend
5. capture
6. common
7. danger
8. afraid
9. borrow
10. office
11. arrow
12. suppose
13. escape
14. whether
15. pillow
16. dinner
17. thirty
18. degree
19. allow
20. corner

1. _____   4. _____

2. _____   5. _____

3. _____   6. _____

✏️ **Write a Character Sketch** Mr. Washington was
kind and encouraging to Ephram. Were you surprised when
Mr. Washington came and played at the concert? How
would describe Mr. Washington to someone who hasn't read
the story?

**On a separate sheet of paper, describe the kind of person
Mr. Washington was. Use Spelling Words from the list.**

Name _____

All the Good News That's Fit to Print

Merry Times, the editor of the *Good News Gazette*, is having a problem with a new reporter, Peter Downhill. He wrote an article that uses many words with negative connotations. Help Merry replace each underlined word with one that has a more positive connotation. Write the new word on the line that has the same number.

Traffic along Maple Street today was <u>horrible</u> , all because
                                                    1

of a family of <u>silly</u> geese. One driver described how traffic
          2

<u>screeched</u> safely to a halt when a <u>stubborn</u> mother goose and her
3   4

family walked across the road. School children <u>escaped</u> their school
                                                            5

bus to watch. The bus driver explained that the <u>nosy</u> students
                                                    6

had never seen geese crossing a road. The students stood on the

sidewalk and <u>screamed</u> hello to the goose and her chicks. A police
          7

officer stepped past the <u>mob</u> of people to <u>push</u> the geese
                          8   9

across the street. Everyone agreed that they would have an <u>odd</u>
                                                                10

story to tell their families.

1. _____   6. _____

2. _____   7. _____

3. _____   8. _____

4. _____   9. _____

5. _____   10. _____

Name _____

Making Comparisons

**Write the correct comparing form of the adjective
in parentheses.**

1. Ephram thought this evening was _____
   than yesterday evening. (warm)

2. During the day, the streets were _____
   than they were at night. (noisy)

3. The _____ sounds of all come from
   a well-played violin. (sweet)

4. On stage, Ephram saw the _____ piano
   he had ever seen. (large)

5. Mr. Washington's fingers were _____
   than they had been before. (stiff)

6. As he thought about playing in public, Ephram felt
   _____ than when he played on the roof. (nervous)

7. The _____ moment of all came when Mr.
   Washington went up on stage with him. (happy)

8. One of the two singers on the program was
   _____ than the other. (thin)

Complete the chart with the correct form of the adjective.

Adjective	Compare 2	Compare 3 or more
hot	→ hotter	
beautiful		→ most beautiful

Name _____

Comparing with Music

Suppose Ephram kept a diary. Help him complete this diary entry by writing the correct forms of the adjectives in the box. Use -er, -est, more, or most.

young	frightened	strong	nice
exciting	familiar	funny	wet

Playing in public yesterday was the _____

thing I have done in my life. When I went up on stage, someone

said I was the _____ person to play at a

concert there. I was a lot _____ than when I

play by myself on the roof. Grandma said that the sound of my

violin was _____ than she ever had heard it.

The _____ thing of all was getting Mr.

Washington to play the piano with me. I discovered that he was

once one of the _____ pianists in our city.

I won't forget this, either. I can't think of anything

_____ than feeling Shiloh's wet nose on my

elbow. That dog has the _____ nose of any

dog I know!

64   Theme 4: **Problem Solvers**

Name _____

Using Comparisons

Good writers are careful to use the correct forms of *good*
and *bad* when comparing two, three, or more.

**Read the following paragraph. Then rewrite it, replacing any
incorrect forms of *good* and *bad*.**

    Hot weather is more bad for a violin than cold weather. The
better temperature of all is around 72°F. One of the worse things
that can happen is for a violin string to break in the middle of a
performance. If the violin bow makes squeaky sounds, the better
thing of all to do is to rub resin on it. Some people think that the
cello has a more good sound than the violin. One thing for sure is
that flat notes sound worst than sharp notes. The baddest sound of
all is a squeaky violin. Personally, I think that the better music of all
is written for the violin.

_____

_____

_____

_____

_____

_____

_____

_____

_____

_____

_____

Name _____

Writing a Message

Use this page to take a telephone *message*.

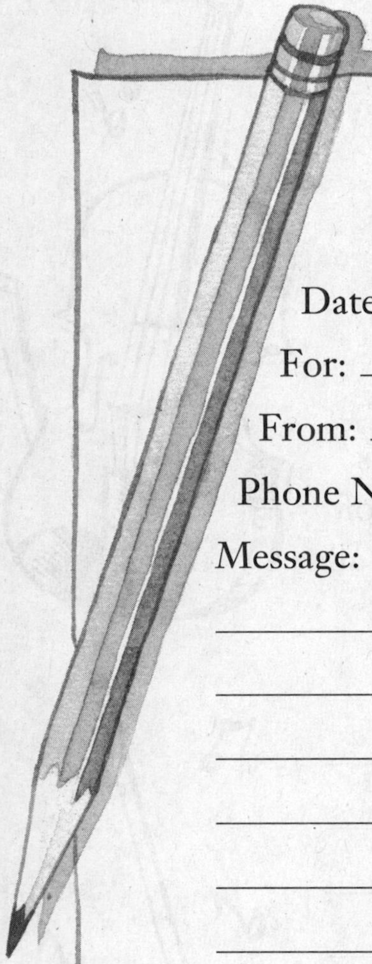

Date: _____ Time: _____

For: _____

From: _____

Phone Number: _____

Message: _____

_____

_____

_____

_____

_____

_____

_____

_____

_____

Message taken by:

_____

Name _____

Using Complete Information

When you take a message, always listen carefully and write the information exactly. Write down all the details. Do not leave anything out.

First "listen" to the following recordings left on a telephone answering machine. Then read the written messages that were taken. Make the written messages complete and exact by correcting any inaccuracies and adding any missing information.

1. Hey, Sam, it's Rick, on Sunday, at 5:00. Cheerleading practice has been changed from Monday and Wednesday to Tuesday and Thursday. Same place, the gym, same time, 3:15. I have to go to the library after practice. Call me, 555-1577.

Date: Sun. **Time:** 5:00
For: Sam **Caller:** Rick
Caller's number: 555-5177

Message: Cheerleading practice time change. Now it's Monday and Thursday. Same time and place. He has to go to the library. Call him.
Message taken by: Tom

2. Hi, Jason. It's me, Yasko, and it's Wednesday, 7:30. Can you bring the cake for the cheerleaders' party? Let me know by Friday. Oh, yeah, the party will be at Suzanne's house after the game on May 18, probably about 5 or 6:00. My number 556-3672. Bye now.

Date: Fri. **Time:** 7:30
For: Jason **Caller:** Yasko
Caller's number: 556-3672

Message: Can you bring the cake and plates for the cheerleaders' party? It's at Yasko's house, after the game on May 8, about 5 or 6:00. Let Yasko know by Fri.
Message taken by: Mom

Name _____

Honest Words

Write each vocabulary word below its definition. Then
unscramble the circled letters to answer the question that follows.

1. person who hires others to do work

2. grassy fields where animals graze

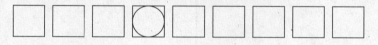

3. an employee who is in charge of other workers

4. people who see something happen

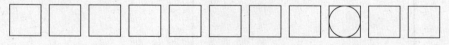

5. very sad

6. in a way that says you believe in yourself

What is a word that describes Juan Verdades?

Vocabulary

foreman
pastures
heartsick
witnesses
employer
confidently

**Monitoring
Student Progress**

Graphic Organizer
Problem/Solution Chart

Problem/Solution Chart

**Fill in this problem solution chart as you read the Paired
Selections.**

	Juan Verdades: The Man Who Couldn't Tell a Lie	*Louis Braille: The Boy Who Invented Books for the Blind*
Who is the main character?		
What is the main character's problem?		
How does the main character solve the problem?		
What are the benefits of solving the problem?		

Name _____

Comparing Settings

Compare the setting of *Juan Verdades* and that of *Marven of the Great North Woods*. Then complete the following chart.

	Juan Verdades	**Marven of the Great North Woods**
What is the setting of the story?	_____ _____	_____ _____
Write at least two details that describe the setting.	1. _____ _____ _____ 2. _____ _____ _____	1. _____ _____ _____ 2. _____ _____ _____
Is the setting important to the story? Why or why not?	_____ _____ _____ _____	_____ _____ _____ _____

Name _____

Braille Words

Choose the vocabulary word that makes the most sense in each sentence. Write the word on the line.

Vocabulary

pinpricks
patterns
succeeding
discouraged
simplified
institute

1. My mom teaches classes at an _____ for the blind.

2. She works hard to make sure that students stay confident and don't get _____ while learning.

3. My mom tells them that _____ at the things they try just takes practice.

4. The students read Braille, _____ of raised dots that stand for letters.

5. Louis Braille invented this system by experimenting with _____ on paper.

6. He _____ an earlier system that was too complicated.

Write two new sentences, using at least one Key Vocabulary word in each sentence.

_____

_____

_____

_____

Name _____

Test Practice

Use the three steps you've learned to choose the best answer for these multiple-choice vocabulary questions about *Louis Braille*. Fill in the circle for the best answer in the answer row at the bottom of each page.

1. Read this sentence from the story: "Often his mother would pack him a lunch of bread and cheese and fruit, and he would wander out to sit on some sunny hillside." What does *wander* mean?

   A get completely lost

   B stumble and fall

   C walk wherever he felt like

   D feel confused

2. Which word means about the same as *rattling* on page 512I?

   F shattering   **H** sneaking

   G gliding   **J** clattering

3. The author writes, "And sometimes he became very, very discouraged." Which word means the opposite of *discouraged*?

   A hopeful   **C** smart

   B brave   **D** frustrated

4. Which word means about the same as *raise* on page 512I?

   F lift   **H** increase

   G nod   **J** hold

ANSWER ROWS   1 Ⓐ Ⓑ Ⓒ Ⓓ   3 Ⓐ Ⓑ Ⓒ Ⓓ

2 Ⓕ Ⓖ Ⓗ Ⓙ   4 Ⓕ Ⓖ Ⓗ Ⓙ

Continue on page 74.

Theme 4: **Problem Solvers**   73

Name _____

Test Practice continued

5. In the last paragraph on page 512J, what does the word *stylus* mean?

   A a pair scissors

   B a lead pencil

   C a sharp, pointed tool for writing

   D a heavy piece of paper

6. Which word means about the same as *eagerly* on page 512L?

   F excitedly

   G slowly

   H sadly

   J impatiently

7. Read this sentence from the story: "He brushed his fingers lightly over the lines of raised dots." What does *brushed* mean?

   A tapped

   B stroked

   C pressed

   D squeezed

8. After Louis demonstrated his alphabet, Dr. Pignier kept murmuring "Amazing." What does the word *murmuring* probably mean?

   F shouting excitedly

   G repeating often

   H scolding angrily

   J saying softly

ANSWER ROWS   5 Ⓐ Ⓑ Ⓒ Ⓓ   7 Ⓐ Ⓑ Ⓒ Ⓓ

               6 Ⓕ Ⓖ Ⓗ Ⓙ   8 Ⓕ Ⓖ Ⓗ Ⓙ

What Would They Do?

Answer each question below with a prediction. Write a detail
from the story that helped you make that prediction. Look back
at the Anthology pages listed below if you need help
remembering story details.

Question	Prediction	Supporting Details
Juan Verdades: The Man Who Couldn't Tell a Lie What do you think Juan would do if don Arturo tried to trick him into lying again? (page 512D)		
Louis Braille: The Boy Who Invented Books for the Blind What do you think Louis would do if he had to come up with a way of improving the way dog guides help people who are blind? (page 512J)		

It's All in the Details

Review the details on the listed Anthology pages. Then write two conclusions that could be drawn from the details.

Details	Possible Conclusions
• Araceli wants to talk to don Ignacio. (Anthology page 512C) • Araceli suggests to her father that she marry Juan Verdades. (page 512F)	1. 2.
• Juan practices telling lies but can't bring himself to lie. (page 512D) • Juan worries all day long about what he will say to don Ignacio. (page 512D)	3. 4.
• Without naming himself, Juan says that a fool picked the apples. (page 512F) • He uses family relations so that don Ignacio knows exactly whom he is talking about. (page 512F)	5. 6.

Name _____

Prefix Puzzle

Read the clues for the puzzle. For each one, choose a word or a word root from the box and add *re-*, *mis-*, or *ex-* to give it the same meaning as the clue. Write the words in the puzzle.

Word Bank

mis- + behave	ex- + claim	re- + capture
deed	hale	fresh
fortune	pand	open
	pend	

Across

2. a bad act
3. to spread out
5. bad luck
7. to make new again
9. to unlock again
10. to breathe out

Down

1. to catch again
4. to act badly
6. to spend or give out
8. to cry out

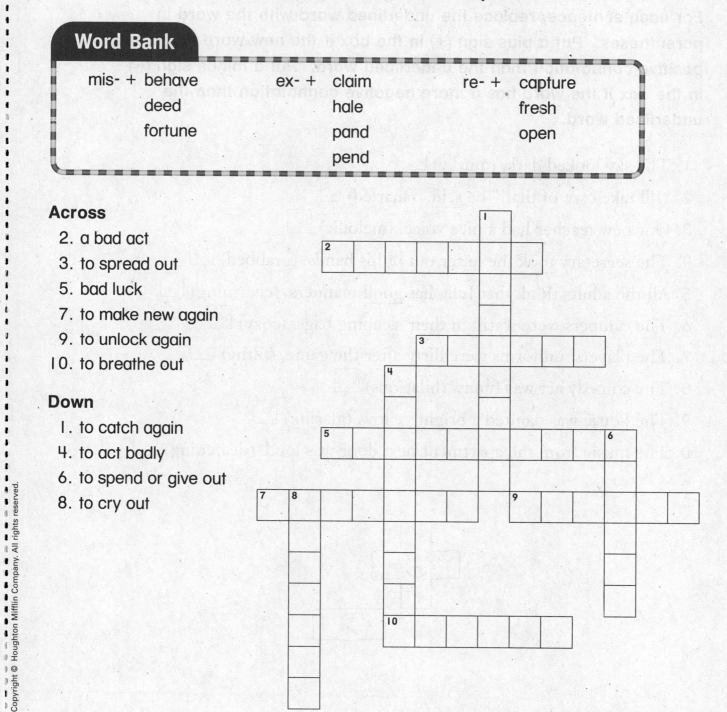

Name _____

Positive or Negative?

Some words can cause a positive reaction in the reader. Other words can cause a negative reaction beyond the dictionary meaning. These positive or negative reactions are *connotations*.

For each sentence, replace the underlined word with the word in parentheses. Put a plus sign (+) in the box if the new word has a more positive connotation than the underlined word. Put a minus sign (−) in the box if the word has a more negative connotation than the underlined word.

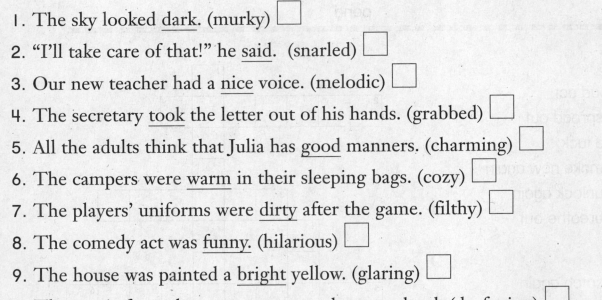

1. The sky looked <u>dark</u>. (murky) ☐
2. "I'll take care of that!" he <u>said</u>. (snarled) ☐
3. Our new teacher had a <u>nice</u> voice. (melodic) ☐
4. The secretary <u>took</u> the letter out of his hands. (grabbed) ☐
5. All the adults think that Julia has <u>good</u> manners. (charming) ☐
6. The campers were <u>warm</u> in their sleeping bags. (cozy) ☐
7. The players' uniforms were <u>dirty</u> after the game. (filthy) ☐
8. The comedy act was <u>funny</u>. (hilarious) ☐
9. The house was painted a <u>bright</u> yellow. (glaring) ☐
10. The music from the apartment next door was <u>loud</u>. (deafening) ☐

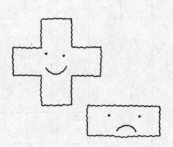

Name _____

Spelling Review

**Write Spelling Words from the list on this page to
answer the questions.**

1–9. Which nine words have the final /ē/ sound?

1. _____   6. _____
2. _____   7. _____
3. _____   8. _____
4. _____   9. _____
5. _____

10–17. Which eight words have the /k/, /ng/, or /kw/ sound?

10. _____   14. _____
11. _____   15. _____
12. _____   16. _____
13. _____   17. _____

18–25. Which eight words have the final /j/, /ĭj/, or /s/
sound?

18. _____   22. _____
19. _____   23. _____
20. _____   24. _____
21. _____   25. _____

26–32. What letters are missing from each word below?
Write each word.

26. of—— _____   30. sup—— _____
27. wheth—— _____   31. cor—— _____
28. af—— _____   32. beau—— _____
29. oth—— _____

Spelling Words

1. village
2. corner
3. office
4. sink
5. squirrel
6. alley
7. whether
8. ridge
9. mistake
10. afraid
11. question
12. other
13. lonely
14. attack
15. thirty
16. blanket
17. monkey
18. twice
19. chance
20. suppose
21. beauty
22. degree
23. crooked
24. honey
25. strange
26. glance
27. twenty
28. cottage
29. since
30. ready

Spelling Spree

Riddles Write the Spelling Word that answers each question.

1. What is a place where people wash dishes?

   _____

2. What word sounds like *weather* and means "if"?

   _____

3. What animal eats nuts and chatters? _____

4. What is a long, narrow edge? _____

5. What is a narrow street? _____

6. What is the place where two lines, meet? _____

7. What kind of sentence are you reading? _____

8. What kind of animal is a baboon? _____

Be a Poet Finish the rhymes by writing a Spelling Word in each blank line. The Spelling Word should rhyme with the underlined word.

9. In their home on the <u>range</u>, those cows are so _____!

10. Don't be _____! That stranger is just the <u>maid</u>.

11. Hold the baseball bat <u>steady</u>. Then your swing will be _____.

12. We've had four cookies, and that should be <u>plenty</u>,

    But Jenny says no — she wants to have _____!

13. The temperature says it is just twenty-<u>three</u>.

    Maybe we should turn the heat up one _____!

14. Do we have enough <u>money</u> to buy that new kind of _____?

15. This is your last _____ to get up and <u>dance</u>.

Spelling Words

1. whether
2. afraid
3. ridge
4. alley
5. squirrel
6. degree
7. strange
8. sink
9. ready
10. question
11. twenty
12. corner
13. monkey
14. honey
15. chance

Name _____

Proofreading and Writing

Proofreading Circle the six misspelled Spelling Words in this plan. Then write each word correctly.

This school year I will try to atak a new problem every day. I want to be reddy to do my best thinking. I will read each question at least twise. I won't just glanss at it. If I have to look at a problem thurty times before I solve it, I will. I suppoze this will be difficult, but I am prepared.

Spelling Words

1. ready
2. mistake
3. crooked
4. glance
5. village
6. cottage
7. other
8. beauty
9. office
10. attack
11. twice
12. suppose
13. thirty
14. blanket
15. lonely

1. _____   4. _____
2. _____   5. _____
3. _____   6. _____

Speech, Speech Use context clues to help you write the Spelling Word that belongs next to each number.

In the 7. _____ of Pineville, there is a narrow, 8. _____ road near the pretty 9. _____ of the Wilson family. It is a quiet and 10. _____ area with natural 11. _____. Some people wanted to tear down the Wilson's house to widen the road. I said we should try this 12. _____ idea: turn the area into a park. At first no one liked the idea. I wanted to get into bed and pull a 13. _____ over my head! Then I met with the mayor in her 14. _____. The mayor agreed that it would be a 15. _____ to widen the road.

7. _____   10. _____   13. _____
8. _____   11. _____   14. _____
9. _____   12. _____   15. _____

Write a Persuasive Paragraph Write a paragraph about a problem and how to solve it. Use the Spelling Review Words.

Name _____

Using Forms of *be*

Complete each sentence by writing the form of *be* that goes with the subject. Use the correct form for the tense named in parentheses.

1. That tree _____ the property of the new ranch owner. (present)

2. Its apples _____ ripe. (present)

3. Juan _____ the guard on the ranch. (past)

4. Araceli and Juan _____ acquaintances. (past)

5. Their conversations _____ repetitious. (past)

6. I _____ a truthful person, too. (present)

7. What _____ Juan's answer to Don Ignacio's question? (past)

8. What _____ your question to me? (present)

9. The apples _____ a gift to a friend. (past)

10. They _____ hers now. (present)

Name _____

Writing Past Tense Forms

Complete each sentence by writing the correct past tense form of the verb named in parentheses.

1. The storyteller _____ many wonderful tales. (know)

2. She _____ a mask with her. (bring)

3. I have _____ a mask like that one. (wear)

4. Many people had _____ to the campfire. (come)

5. A ranger _____ more logs on the fire. (throw)

6. Soon the storyteller had _____ her tale. (begin)

7. I had _____ very tired by then. (grow)

8. I _____ my seat to another person. (give)

9. On the way back to the cabin, I _____ my glasses from their case. (take)

10. They had _____ somehow, much to my dismay. (break)

Name _____

All About a Poem

Read the poem. Then use words from the box to complete the description below.

Vocabulary

beats
imagery
lines
repetition
rhyme
rhythm
sense words
stanzas

The Hungry Toaster

I slip a slice of soft white bread
Into my toaster's jaws.
It grabs the bread and pulls it down
With greedy metal paws.

I think my toaster would prefer
Another kind of snack,
Because a minute later,
It throws my bread right back.

This poem has eight _____ arranged in two

_____. As you say the first line, tap out four strong

_____. The whole poem has a bouncy, playful

_____. The words *jaws* and *paws* and the words *snack*

and *back* _____. Listen for the _____

of the beginning sounds in *slip* and *slice*. The poet compares a

toaster to a hungry animal. This comparison is an example of

_____. The poet also uses _____

such as *soft* and *white*.

Name _____

Poetry Elements Chart

ELEMENT	POEM TITLE	EXAMPLES
Rhyme: similar end sounds <u>Examples:</u> *round/frowned, white/tonight*		
Sense Words: words that appeal to sight, smell, taste, touch, hearing <u>Examples:</u> *glisten, thorny, sour*		
Figurative Language: imaginative comparisons between unlike things <u>Examples:</u> *Spring arrived laughing. Flowers covered the hillside like a quilt.*		
Wordplay: clever or funny uses of meanings, sounds, and nonsense <u>Example:</u> *I scream/You scream/We all scream for ice cream.*		

Name _____

May the Best Poems Win!

You are hosting an awards ceremony for poetry. Choose a different poem from this theme to receive each award. Explain why each poem won that prize, giving an example from that poem.

Best Rhythm Award

Winning Poem: _____

Why: _____

_____

Example: _____

_____

Best Rhyme Award

Winning Poem: _____

Why: _____

_____

Example: _____

_____

Best Imagery Award

Winning Poem: _____

Why: _____

_____

Example: _____

_____

Name _____

Comparing Poems

Think about the elements of poetry. Choose three poems to study. Then complete the chart below.

	(poem title)	(poem title)	(poem title)
What kind of language is used in the poem?			
Does the poem express a feeling? If so, describe it.			
What images are in the poem?			

Tell which of these poems is your favorite and why.

_____

_____

_____

Name _____

Elements of a Poem

Answer questions 1–4 after reading the poem below.

The Crocodile

1 If you should meet a crocodile,
2 Don't take a stick and poke him;
3 Ignore the welcome in his smile,
4 Be careful not to stroke him.

5 For as he sleeps upon the Nile,
6 He grows thinner and thinner;
7 And whene'er you meet a crocodile
8 He's ready for his dinner.

—Anonymous

1. Which lines end with words that rhyme? What are the words?

_____

_____

2. Is there any repetition in this poem? Explain.

_____

3. How can you tell that line 3 has personification?

_____

4. What do you think is the poet's purpose? Explain.

_____

**Read these two lines from a poem. Then read the list of
elements. Circle any elements you find in the lines.**

The skaters glide, glide, glide like swans.
They swirl on the cold, smooth ice.

5. Elements

rhythm   repetition

rhyme   metaphor

imagery   personification

sense words   simile

Focus on Poetry

Structural Analysis Prefixes
*re-, mis-, ex-, pre-, con-,
com-*

The Proper Prefix

Read each sentence. Look at the prefixes in the two words in parentheses. Write the word in parentheses that belongs in the sentence. If you are unsure of meaning, use a dictionary.

1. Before a movie comes to theaters, you can watch scenes
   in a _____. (preview, review)

2. The cookies tasted like cardboard because Kay
   _____the recipe. (misread, reread)

3. Have you _____ the leftover chicken?
   (preheated, reheated)

4. A red sock and a blue sock are a _____.
   (mismatch, rematch)

5. When Candy Lim married Arthur Kane, she decided to
   _____ her own last name. (retain, contain)

6. The votes are close in the election, so we need a
   _____. (miscount, recount)

7. The friends _____ their hands to shake on the
   agreement. (extended, pretended)

8. Dentists know how to _____ teeth that have
   decayed. (retract, extract)

9. The children sang a song they _____ by
   themselves. (composed, exposed)

10. The speaker _____ by thanking everyone who
    had come to listen. (concluded, excluded)

pre-

mis-

re-

ex-

𝕮𝕺𝕸-

CON-

Name _____

More VCCV Words

A VCCV word is divided into syllables between the consonants unless the consonants form a cluster or make one sound.

VC | CV
yel | low
gar | den

V | CCV
se | cret

VCC | V
pack | age

1. garden
2. yellow
3. rather
4. secret
5. package
6. apron
7. narrow
8. chicken
9. gather
10. declare
11. entire
12. bucket
13. rabbit
14. engine
15. nothing
16. person
17. silver
18. number
19. rocket
20. limber

Write each Spelling Word under the heading that shows where the word is divided into syllables. Draw a line between the syllables.

vc | cv

_____
_____
_____
_____
_____
_____
_____

v | ccv

_____
_____

vcc | v

_____
_____
_____

Name _____

Spelling Spree

Crossword Puzzle Write the Spelling Words that fit the clues to complete the puzzle.

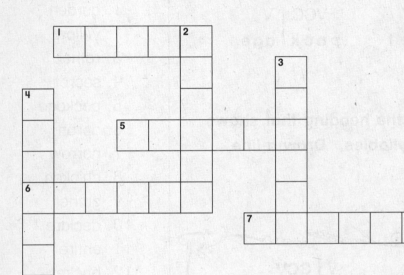

1. garden
2. yellow
3. rather
4. secret
5. package
6. apron
7. narrow
8. chicken
9. gather
10. declare
11. entire
12. bucket
13. rabbit
14. engine
15. nothing
16. person
17. silver
18. number
19. rocket
20. limber

Across

1. A cook wears this.
5. Another name for a bunny
6. Instead of
7. A boy or a girl

Down

2. a 3 or a 5
3. All
4. Opposite of *wide*

Alphabet Dash Write the Spelling Word that fits in alphabetical order between the other two words.

8. kitchen, _____, nail

9. early, _____, enter

10. nut, _____, pencil

11. chunky, _____, edge

12. button, _____, daisy

13. riddle, _____, ruler

14. away, _____, change

15. navy, _____, now

Name _____

Proofreading and Writing

Proofreading Circle the five misspelled Spelling Words in these riddle poems. Then write each word correctly. (Riddle answers are upside-down at the bottom of this page.)

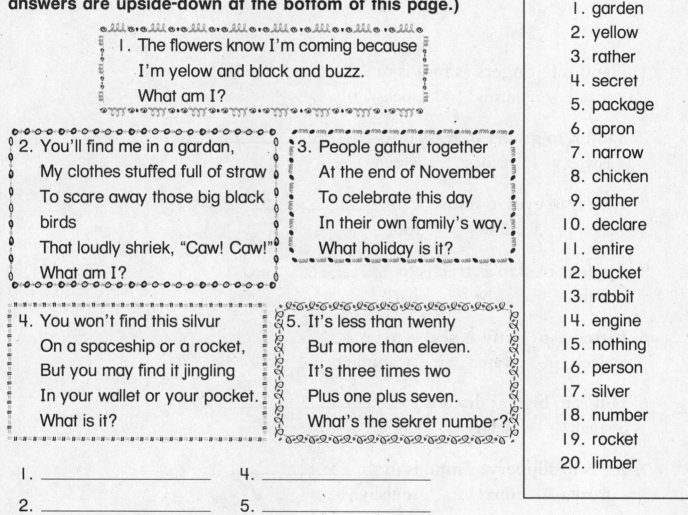

1. The flowers know I'm coming because
   I'm yelow and black and buzz.
   What am I?

2. You'll find me in a gardan,
   My clothes stuffed full of straw
   To scare away those big black birds
   That loudly shriek, "Caw! Caw!"
   What am I?

3. People gathur together
   At the end of November
   To celebrate this day
   In their own family's way.
   What holiday is it?

4. You won't find this silvur
   On a spaceship or a rocket,
   But you may find it jingling
   In your wallet or your pocket.
   What is it?

5. It's less than twenty
   But more than eleven.
   It's three times two
   Plus one plus seven.
   What's the sekret number?

1. _____
2. _____
3. _____
4. _____
5. _____

✏️ **Write a Riddle Poem** Think about topics for riddle poems. You can use everyday objects such as chalk, a calendar, a fire hydrant, or different animals. On a separate sheet of paper, write two riddle poems. Use Spelling Words from the list. Then trade poems with a classmate and guess the answers to each other's riddles.

1. bee   2. scarecrow   3. Thanksgiving Day   4. coin   5. 14

Name _____

Let's Compare

**Decide how the first two items are related in each analogy.
Write the word that best completes the analogy.**

1. **Hand** is to **fingers** as **foot** is to _____.
   toes   arms   socks

2. **Sand** is to **grains** as **grass** is to _____.
   lawns   blades   green

3. **Face** is to **eyes** as **house** is to _____.
   see   windows   roof

4. **Apple** is to **skin** as **tree** is to _____.
   fruit   grow   bark

5. **Kitten** is to **fluffy** as **seal** is to _____.
   sleek   water   swimming

6. **Hill** is to **high** as **ditch** is to _____.
   small   deep   dig

7. **Ice** is to **slippery** as **mud** is to _____.
   frozen   dirty   squishy

8. **Bear** is to **brown** as **chick** is to _____.
   fuzzy   hen   yellow

9. **Frog** is to **leaping** as **penguin** is to _____.
   bird   flying   waddling

10. **Paragraph** is to **sentences** as **poem** is to _____.
    lines   recite   write

Name _____

Choosing the Better Adjective

Choose the better adjective to complete each line of the poem.
Look for adjectives that are exact in meaning and make sense.
Write each word you choose.

The _____ trees are black
      big   enormous

Against the _____ moon.
        pale   pretty

A _____ breeze blows softly
    little   gentle

And hums a _____ tune.
      good   peaceful

A _____ squirrel climbs a tree
   sleepy   pleasant

And rubs one _____ eye.
        tiny   small

In its _____ nest, it hears
     cozy   nice

The _____ lullaby.
    great   restful

Name _____

Adding Exact Adjectives

**Use adjectives from the box to expand each sentence. Choose
adjectives that are exact and make sense. Some adjectives
will not be used. Write your choice on the line.**

1. My grandma's attic is dark and _____.

2. Up there I found a book with a _____ and
   gold cover.

3. I read poems by a wise and _____ poet.

4. I opened a box of old-fashioned, _____ fans.

5. Letters were hidden in a heavy _____ trunk.

| **Adjectives** |
| lacy |
| big |
| clever |
| gloomy |
| nice |
| wooden |
| violet |
| good |

**Use your own adjectives to complete this poem, one
adjective for each line.**

Grandpa's basement is _____ and cold.

I go there when I feel _____ and bold.

The air down there is _____ and wet,

But there's an old toy I want to get!

Slowly I open the _____ door.

Oh! Some _____ spiders crawl on the floor!

Name _____

More Comparing

**Use proofreading marks to correct the fourteen errors in
capitalization, punctuation, and comparing forms of
adjectives in this description of a school poetry contest.**

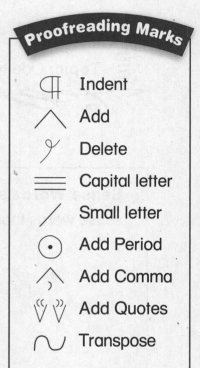

Proofreading Marks

⊓	Indent
∧	Add
ᵞ	Delete
═	Capital letter
/	Small letter
⊙	Add Period
∧	Add Comma
ᵛᵛ ᵛᵛ	Add Quotes
∼	Transpose

Example: let me tell you about the ~~most~~ funniest contest
of the year.

our class held a contest to find the more
strangest poem in the fourth grade. The first
poem was the longer poem in the contest The
second poem was more shorter than the first.
my favorite poem described the most smartest
cat in the world. The judges picked a strangest
poem than that one The poet told about a
carrot more bigger than a whale A rabbit more
enormouser than the carrot tried to eat it That
certainly is the most strangest poem of all!

WORLD'S STRANGEST POEM

Name _____

Planning a Descriptive Poem

Topic: Ode to _____

Sense Words show what I see, hear, touch, taste, and smell. Here are some
sense words that fit with my topic.

Figurative Language includes personification, similes, and metaphors. Here
are some imaginative comparisons I might put in my poem.

Exact Details will show exactly what I am describing. Here are some details I
may include.

Name _____

Similes and Metaphors

Poets use figurative comparisons to point out likenesses between
unlike things. Two kinds of figurative comparisons are similes and
metaphors. A simile uses *like* or *as*. A metaphor says that one thing
is another.

Read the poem. Then answer the questions about it.

Wind Tree

In the field, the tree stands like a harp.
The branches are the strings
that the wind blows through.
The leaves are the notes
that fly from the strings,
and the music sounds like rushing water.

1. What are the two similes in the poem?

   _____

   _____

2. What are the branches compared to? What does that metaphor
   help you imagine?

   _____

   _____

3. What other metaphor is included? What two things does it
   compare?

   _____

   _____

Name _____

Heroes

Fill in the information to show what you think about heroes.

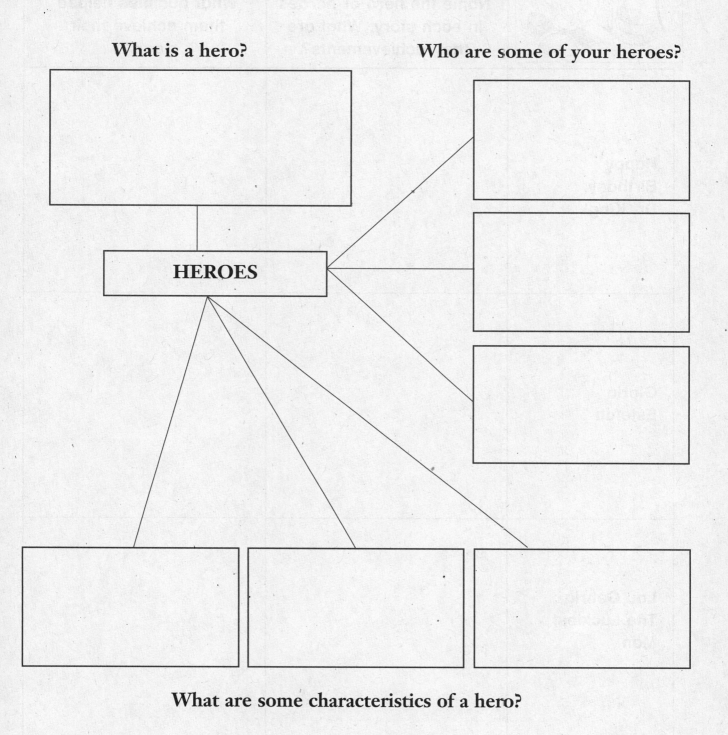

What is a hero?

Who are some of your heroes?

HEROES

What are some characteristics of a hero?

Name _____

Heroes

	Name the hero or heroes in each story. What are their achievements?	What qualities helped them achieve their goals?
Happy Birthday, Dr. King!		
Gloria Estefan		
Lou Gehrig: The Luckiest Man		

Name _____

Civil Rights Crossword

Complete the crossword puzzle using words from the vocabulary box.

Vocabulary

boycott　　civil rights　　fare　　protest　　stupendous

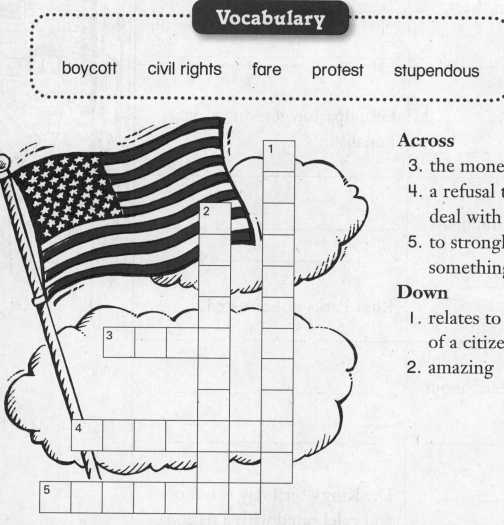

Across

3. the money paid to travel
4. a refusal to use, buy from, or deal with a company
5. to strongly object to something

Down

1. relates to the legal privileges of a citizen
2. amazing

Write a sentence using at least two of the vocabulary words.

_____

_____

Name _____

Cause and Effect Chart

Cause	Effect
page 536 Jamal gets a note from the principal.	_____ _____ _____
page 539 _____ _____	Grandpa Joe gets angry at Jamal.
page 541 Jamal apologizes to Grandpa Joe for fighting. _____ _____	_____ _____ Rosa Parks got arrested.
page 542 African Americans heard about Rosa Parks's arrest.	_____ _____
page 544 _____ _____ _____	Dr. King's birthday is honored and celebrated with a national holiday.
page 547 Dad explains to Jamal that Dr. King worked in peaceful ways.	_____ _____

Name _____

Knowing Dr. King

Read and answer the questions.

1. Why was Grandpa Joe so angry that Jamal got into a fight to sit in the back of the bus?

_____

_____

2. Which two famous African Americans did Jamal and Grandpa Joe talk about?

_____

_____

3. What did Jamal's father say about the way Dr. King made things happen?

_____

_____

4. What was the Montgomery Bus Boycott?

_____

_____

5. Dr. King become a leader of what movement?

_____

_____

6. What did Jamal decide to do for the Martin Luther King, Jr., assembly?

_____

_____

Name _____

The Effects of Hard Work

Read the story below and then complete the chart on the next page.

The Family Business

Pedro never thought he would miss collecting old newspapers from his neighbors and recycling them. As a kid, he hated spending one Saturday every two weeks picking up the papers and taking them to the recycling center. The newspapers made him dirty. He missed playing games with his friends on those days. He especially didn't like working in the hot sun of the summer. He used to think there wasn't anything good about the job. He thought it was a waste of his time.

But now that he was moving with his family to a new neighborhood, he thought back on all the good things that happened because of the job. His sisters, who started the business, each saved enough money to pay for their own summer vacations to Europe. Pedro was able to buy a stereo for his room and send himself to summer camp.

"Hey, Pedro! Come in here please," his mother called from the kitchen. "Grampa's on the phone and he wants to say good-bye."

"Hello, Grampa! I was just thinking about the paper recycling business you convinced Anna and Katrina to begin. It sure brought us many good things."

"I'm glad to hear that, Pedro," his grandfather said. "It just goes to show you that all it takes is a good idea."

Name _____

The Effects of Hard Work

continued

Complete the chart below based on "The Family Business."

Cause	Effect
_____ _____ _____ _____ _____ _____ _____ _____ _____	Pedro didn't like his recycling job.
His sisters saved enough money to go to Europe. He bought a stereo. He paid for summer camp.	_____ _____

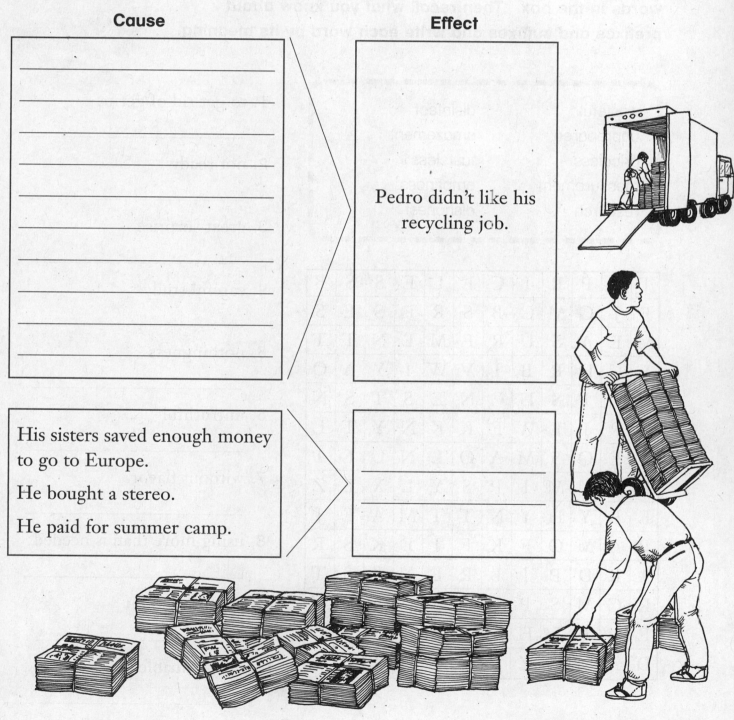

Name _____

Searching for Prefixes and Suffixes

In the puzzle below, find and circle the hidden words in the box. Then recall what you know about prefixes and suffixes and write each word by its meaning.

wasteful	disinfect
unprepared	amazement
priceless	tasteless
measurement	emptiness
research	dishonest

T	V	P	R	I	C	E	L	E	S	S	B
F	J	G	M	G	B	S	R	E	S	E	S
M	E	A	S	U	R	E	M	E	N	T	T
Y	U	D	R	B	I	V	W	I	Y	A	O
U	D	I	S	H	O	N	E	S	T	S	N
N	R	I	E	W	E	K	K	N	Y	T	L
P	E	Q	S	M	A	O	L	N	U	E	I
R	S	U	M	I	P	S	Y	L	X	L	Z
E	E	Y	H	Y	N	T	T	M	A	E	J
P	A	M	O	F	K	F	I	E	K	S	R
A	R	D	P	I	B	R	E	N	F	S	T
R	C	M	S	P	F	N	E	C	E	U	M
E	H	P	L	H	H	K	A	H	T	S	L
D	A	M	A	Z	E	M	E	N	T	B	S

1. to get rid of germs

   _____

2. not ready

   _____

3. great surprise

   _____

4. careful study

   _____

5. nothingness

   _____

6. untruthful

   _____

7. without flavor

   _____

8. using more than is needed

   _____

9. size or amount

   _____

10. very valuable

   _____

Name _____

Words with a Prefix or a Suffix

A **prefix** is a word part added to the beginning of a base word. A **suffix** is a word part added to the end of a base word. Both prefixes and suffixes add meaning.

Prefixes: **re**build, **dis**like, **un**lucky

Suffixes: sick**ness**, treat**ment**, beauti**ful**, care**less**

► In the starred word *awful*, the *e* was dropped from the base word *awe* before the suffix *-ful* was added.

Write each Spelling Word under its prefix or suffix.

1. redo
2. treatment
3. rebuild
4. discolor
5. careless
6. dislike
7. sickness
8. beautiful
9. unlucky
10. awful*
11. reread
12. unsure
13. movement
14. peaceful
15. unpaid
16. distrust
17. kindness
18. useless
19. displease
20. powerful

re-

_____

_____

-ness

_____

_____

-ment

_____

_____

dis-

_____

_____

_____

-ful

_____

_____

_____

_____

un-

_____

_____

_____

-less

_____

_____

_____

Theme 5: **Heroes**   109

Name _____

Spelling Spree

Finding Words Each word below is hidden in a Spelling Word. Write the Spelling Word.

Example: hop *hopeful*

1. ace _____

2. plea _____

3. eat _____

4. rust _____

5. are _____

6. owe _____

7. red _____

8. disco _____

9. aid _____

10. kin _____

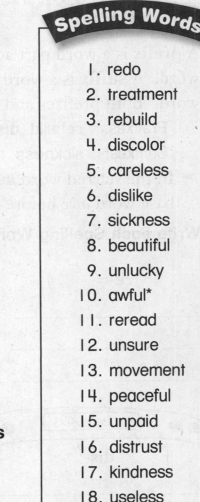

Spelling Words

1. redo
2. treatment
3. rebuild
4. discolor
5. careless
6. dislike
7. sickness
8. beautiful
9. unlucky
10. awful*
11. reread
12. unsure
13. movement
14. peaceful
15. unpaid
16. distrust
17. kindness
18. useless
19. displease
20. powerful

Questions Write the Spelling Word that best answers each question.

11. What is an antonym for *health*?

12. What kind of object serves no purpose?

13. What is a milder word for *hate*?

14. What might you do if your house burns down?

15. What is a synonym for *terrible*?

16. What is another word for "unfortunate"?

11. _____   14. _____

12. _____   15. _____

13. _____   16. _____

Proofreading and Writing

Proofreading Circle the four misspelled Spelling Words in this book review. Then write each word correctly.

Are you unshure why we honor Martin Luther King, Jr., with a holiday? If so, get hold of a copy of *Happy Birthday, Dr. King!* Jamal Wilson is the main character of this beutiful but powerful picture book. As Jamal learns about the civil rights moovement, readers do, too. Believe me, you won't read this book only once. You'll rerread it many times!

Spelling Words

1. redo
2. treatment
3. rebuild
4. discolor
5. careless
6. dislike
7. sickness
8. beautiful
9. unlucky
10. awful*
11. reread
12. unsure
13. movement
14. peaceful
15. unpaid
16. distrust
17. kindness
18. useless
19. displease
20. powerful

1. _____   3. _____

2. _____   4. _____

✏️ **Write Copy for a Book Jacket** Many books have jackets, paper covers that protect the hard covers. Book jacket copy tells some details about the book. However, it doesn't tell enough to spoil the book for readers.

On a separate sheet of paper, write copy for a book jacket for your favorite book. Tell only enough to make readers want to read the book. Use Spelling Words from the list.

Theme 5: **Heroes**   111

Name _____

Crossword Prefixes

Use the base words and prefixes in the box to make new words that match the clues. Enter the new words where they belong in the crossword puzzle.

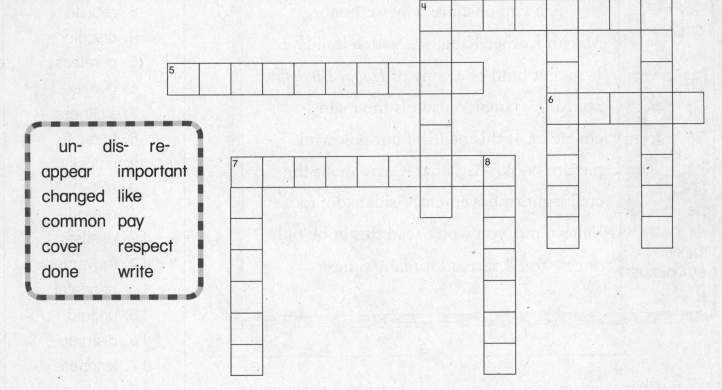

un- dis- re-
appear   important
changed   like
common   pay
cover   respect
done   write

Across

2. The job isn't finished, so it is _____.

4. Something very different may be _____.

5. If you act rudely, you show _____.

6. When you give money back to people, you _____ them.

7. Something you lose may just seem to _____.

Down

1. If something doesn't matter much, it's _____.

3. It's no different than before, so it's _____.

4. Take your cap off and _____ your head.

7. If you don't care much for something you _____ it.

8. When you do your lesson over, you _____ it.

Name _____

Replacing Nouns with Pronouns

For each sentence below, write a subject pronoun to replace the word or words given in parentheses. Write your sentence on the lines provided.

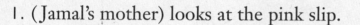

1. (Jamal's mother) looks at the pink slip.
   _____

2. (Jamal) was in trouble now.
   _____

3. His mother asked Jamal, "Did (Jamal) get in trouble today?"
   _____

4. (Alisha) was not home yet.
   _____

5. (Jamal's classmates) are planning a celebration for Dr. King.
   _____

6. (Grandpa Joe) was angry with Jamal for fighting.
   _____

7. (Jamal) listened to Grandpa Joe's story about the boycott.
   _____

8. (Grandpa Joe and his wife) boycotted the buses.
   _____

In Search of a Subject Pronoun

Suppose that Jamal's class is having a discussion about what to do for the Martin Luther King, Jr., celebration. Write a subject pronoun to replace the word or words in parentheses.

Mrs. Gordon: Jamal says that (Jamal) _____ thinks a skit would be a good idea.

Jamal: Yes, that way (the rest of the class and I) _____ could all have a part.

Albert: How about the subject of the skit? What will (the subject) _____ be?

Mrs. Gordon: Jamal says that (Jamal) _____ has an idea.

Jamal: Well, (Jamal) _____ thought that we could do a skit about two boys on a bus. (The two boys) _____ are arguing over an empty seat at the back of the bus.

Frieda: That skit sounds like a good idea. (The skit) _____ is about Mrs. Parks's fight for civil rights.

Margie: Mrs. Gordon, would (Mrs. Gordon) _____ direct the skit?

Mrs. Gordon: Yes, (Mrs. Gordon) _____ would be happy to do that.

Billy: Aminta should have a part. (Aminta) _____ can play the part of the bus driver.

Name _____

Sentence Combining with Subject Pronouns

When two sentences have different subjects but the same predicate, you can combine them into one sentence with a compound subject.

Read the sentences below. Then rewrite them, combining each pair of sentences into one sentence with a compound subject. Use the joining word in parentheses to write the new sentences.

1. She gave the bus driver money for a ticket. I gave the bus driver money for a ticket. (and)

_____

2. You were there to hear the entire speech. They were there to hear the entire speech. (and)

_____

3. She will recite part of the speech from memory. You will recite part of the speech from memory. (or)

_____

4. They listened to the words carefully. I listened to the words carefully. (and)

_____

5. She will prepare a report about Martin Luther King, Jr. I will prepare a report about Martin Luther King, Jr. (or)

_____

Name _____

Writing an Information Paragraph

Use this graphic organizer to help you plan your information paragraph about a leader you admire. Tell why you admire this person, and what he or she did that is admirable, and why you chose this leader.

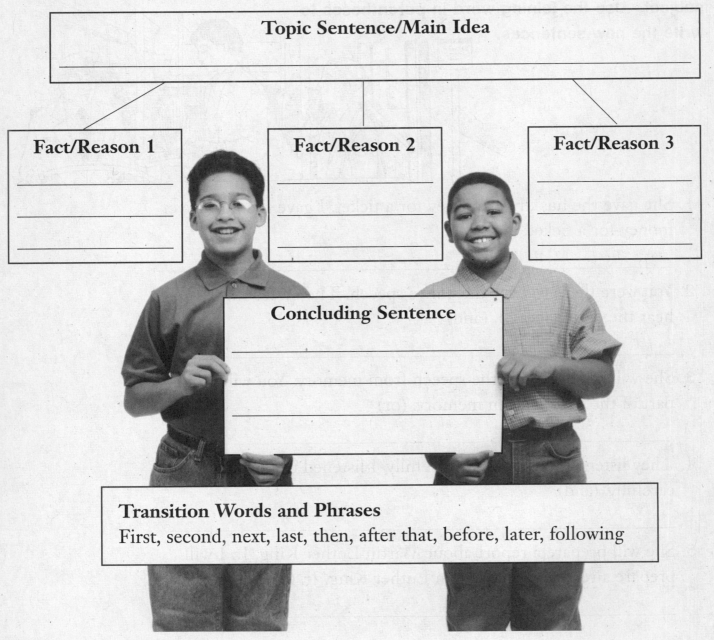

Topic Sentence/Main Idea
_____

Fact/Reason 1
_____
_____
_____

Fact/Reason 2
_____
_____
_____

Fact/Reason 3
_____
_____
_____

Concluding Sentence
_____
_____
_____

Transition Words and Phrases
First, second, next, last, then, after that, before, later, following

Name _____

Using Facts

Good writers use facts to support the main idea of an information paragraph. To do so, they organize them in different ways.

► Writers use chronological order to put events in the order in which they happen.

► Writers use spatial order to describe how things look.

► Writers use the order of importance to organize facts from least to most important or from most to least important.

Read the following clusters of facts. Then decide on a main idea and use the facts to write a paragraph of information. Identify the kind of order you used.

1. On Tuesday, the math teacher gives us a mini-test.
   We have a history test on Wednesday.
   Monday afternoon, we have a special art class.
   Every Friday, there's a spelling quiz.

   _____

   _____

   _____

   _____

2. The third graders sang a medley of civil rights songs.
   Jamal's skit was the hit of the Dr. Martin Luther King, Jr., assembly.
   Everyone talked about it for weeks.
   The first graders recited Dr. King's "I Have a Dream" speech.

   _____

   _____

   _____

   _____

Name _____

Revising Your Personal Essay

Reread your personal essay. Put a checkmark in the box for each sentence that describes your paper. Use this page to help you revise.

Rings the Bell

- [ ] My essay focuses on a single opinion, supported by reasons and details.

- [ ] My reasons and details are organized in separate paragraphs, with clear topic sentences.

- [ ] I wrote a strong introduction and conclusion.

- [ ] I used exact words that show readers how I feel.

- [ ] Sentences flow smoothly. There are few mistakes.

Getting Stronger

- [ ] My opinion is clear, but I need more reasons or details.

- [ ] My paragraphs could be organized better.

- [ ] My introduction and conclusion could be stronger.

- [ ] My words are too vague. I don't always tell how I feel.

- [ ] Some sentences are choppy. There are a few mistakes.

Try Harder

- [ ] My opinion is not clear. There are few reasons or details.

- [ ] My paper is a list of thoughts.

- [ ] There is no introduction or conclusion.

- [ ] I used the same word many times. My writing sounds flat.

- [ ] Most sentences are choppy. There are many mistakes.

Name _____

Pronoun Reference

Pronouns are words that replace nouns. Write the word or words that the underlined pronoun refers to in each exercise.

1. I would love to start my own magazine. <u>It</u> would be called *Cartoon*.

2. This magazine would be all cartoons. <u>They</u> would be on every page.

3. I would write all the articles for the magazine. My friend Jimmy would edit <u>them</u>.

4. "You write the articles," Jimmy says. "Let me edit <u>them</u>."

5. Jimmy and I love those old Bugs Bunny cartoons. We have made tapes of <u>them</u>.

6. We also love newspaper cartoons. Jimmy collects <u>them</u>.

7. We both really like *Peanuts* by Charles Schulz. <u>He</u> had his characters say such funny things.

8. My sister would like to interview Matt Groening. <u>She</u> thinks he is the best cartoonist of all.

9. Do you know who Matt Groening is? <u>He</u> is the creator of *The Simpsons*.

10. The characters on the show are based on real people. <u>They</u> have the same names as people in Groening's family.

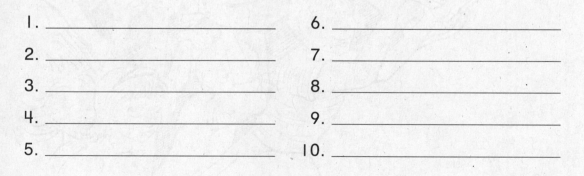

1. _____   6. _____

2. _____   7. _____

3. _____   8. _____

4. _____   9. _____

5. _____   10. _____

Name _____

Spelling Words

Words Often Misspelled Look for familiar spelling patterns to help you remember how to spell the Spelling Words on this page. Think carefully about the parts that you find hard to spell in each word.

Write the missing letters in the Spelling Words below.

1. br ___ ___ ___ ___ t
2. en ___ ___ ___ ___
3. b ___ y
4. ___ ___ ess
5. Sat ___ ___ day
6. Jan ___ ___ ___ y
7. Feb ___ ___ ___ ___ y
8. favor ___ ___ ___

9. l ___ ing
10. t ___ ing
11. ___ round
12. swim ___ ing
13. h ___ ___ rd
14. a ___ ___ o
15. tr ___ ___ ___

1. brought
2. enough
3. buy
4. guess
5. Saturday
6. January
7. February
8. favorite
9. lying
10. tying
11. around
12. swimming
13. heard
14. also
15. tried

Study List On a separate piece of paper, write each Spelling Word. Check your spelling against the words on the list.

Spelling Spree

Opposites Write a Spelling Word that means the opposite of the underlined words.

1. I was <u>telling the truth</u> when I said that I knew how to fly a plane. _____

2. We went to the store to <u>sell</u> some groceries to get ready for the big storm. _____

3. She <u>didn't attempt</u> to call you to let you know what the homework was. _____

4. Isn't your <u>most disliked</u> singer playing a concert next month? _____

5. It was <u>nowhere near</u> ten o'clock when we finished watching the movie. _____

Spelling Words

1. brought
2. enough
3. buy
4. guess
5. Saturday
6. January
7. February
8. favorite
9. lying
10. tying
11. around
12. swimming
13. heard
14. also
15. tried

Crack the Code Some Spelling Words have been written in the code below. Use the code to figure out each word. Then write the words correctly.

CODE: u d m r s i q o b a c e f z v t y n p h
LETTER: a b c d e f g h i j l m n o r s t u w y

6. Aufnuvh   9. osuvr   12. sfznqo   15. qnstt

7. dvznqoy   10. yhbfq   13. uctz

8. tpbeebfq   11. Isdvnuvh   14. Tuynvruh

6. _____   10. _____   14. _____

7. _____   11. _____   15. _____

8. _____   12. _____

9. _____   13. _____

Theme 5: **Heroes**   121

Name _____

Proofreading and Writing

Proofreading Circle the four misspelled Spelling Words in this inscription on a statue. Then write each word correctly.

This statue is in honor of the accomplishment of Elmer Fitzgerald on Saterday, February 21, 1920. On that day, he single-handedly caught enouf fish to feed his entire village for three months. Unfortunately, before the fish could be brot back to shore, they were all eaten by sharks. Elmer treid to drive the sharks off with his fishing pole, but there were just too many of them. At least, that's what Elmer told us.

Spelling Words

1. brought
2. enough
3. buy
4. guess
5. Saturday
6. January
7. February
8. favorite
9. lying
10. tying
11. around
12. swimming
13. heard
14. also
15. tried

1. _____

2. _____

3. _____

4. _____

Write a Round-Robin Story Get together in a small group with other students. Then write a story about a hero, with each of you writing one sentence at a time. Use a Spelling Word from the list in each sentence.

122   Theme 5: **Heroes**

Name _____

Be a Recording Star!

Complete the sentences in this ad for a recording company.
Use each vocabulary word once.

Vocabulary

career	contract	demonstrated	eventually
specializes	tireless	worldwide	

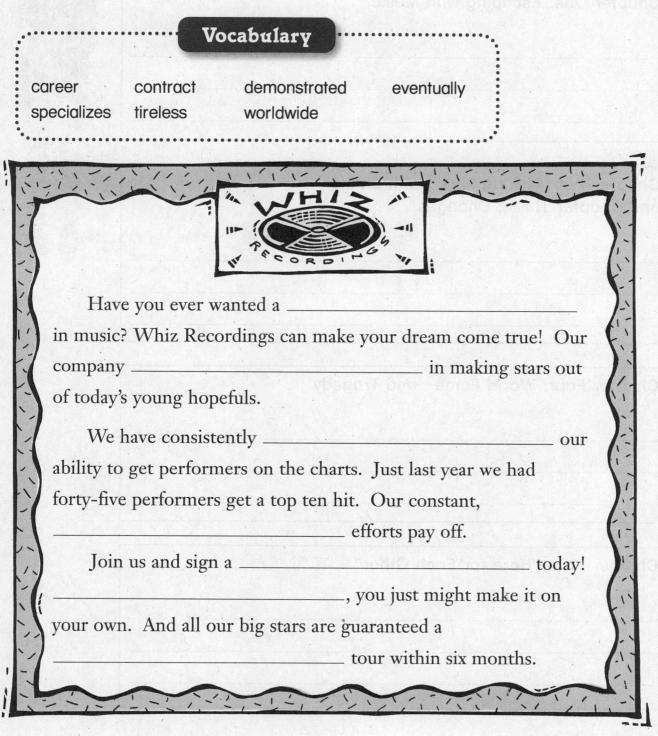

Have you ever wanted a _____

in music? Whiz Recordings can make your dream come true! Our

company _____ in making stars out

of today's young hopefuls.

We have consistently _____ our

ability to get performers on the charts. Just last year we had

forty-five performers get a top ten hit. Our constant,

_____ efforts pay off.

Join us and sign a _____ today!

_____, you just might make it on

your own. And all our big stars are guaranteed a

_____ tour within six months.

Name _____

Judgments Chart

Why Might Someone Call Gloria Estefan a "Hero"?

Chapter One: Escaping with Music

_____

_____

_____

**Chapter Two: Making Music with Emilio
and Chapter Three: Changes**

_____

_____

_____

Chapter Four: World Fame—and Tragedy

_____

_____

_____

Chapter Five: "Here for Each Other"

_____

_____

_____

Name _____

Music World

Help the reporter from *Music World* write an article on
Gloria Estefan by answering his questions about the
star. Use complete sentences.

**I hear you have read a lot about Gloria Fajardo Estefan.
Tell me something about her childhood, up to age 16.**

_____

_____

_____

**Tell me the story of how Gloria became a member of Emilio
Estefan's band—and how they fell in love.**

_____

_____

_____

**In your opinion, what were Gloria's most important
achievements before her accident in 1990? What are the most
important things she has done since then?**

Before the accident: _____

_____

_____

Since the accident: _____

_____

_____

What can a young person learn from Gloria Estefan?

_____

_____

_____

Name _____

Judge for Yourself

Read the story. Then complete the following page.

The Singing Cubs

My friends and I have a band that we call The Singing Cubs, and we're planning on entering the school talent show this year. I'm Bobby, the group's lead guitar player and singer. My friend Megan also plays the guitar, and Ralphie is our drummer.

The day before the talent show, the principal announced that all assignments had to be turned in first thing in the morning for those students participating in the show. We knew it would be a busy night.

Ralphie's parents decided they couldn't stand his messy room any longer. They said he needed to clean it up or no show. Then to make matters worse, my mother got sick and I had to help with dinnertime. I was so busy. I washed, carried, served, and washed again. Finally, dinner was over and I could begin my homework.

After dinner, I finished most of my homework. Then I called Megan because I needed help on my book report. She was also hard at work on her report. She needed help on it too. We talked a few things over and were soon ready to finish the reports on our own.

Then Ralphie called. He said, "There's no way I can get my room clean tonight. It's too messy." Both Megan and I went to Ralphie's house and worked hard on his room until it was spotless. Nothing could stand in our way now!

When it came time to perform the next day, we were exhausted but proud of ourselves. Mr. Major introduced us as "The Hard-Working Singing Cubs" and looked pleased with all that we had accomplished. Our parents were sitting in the front row, beaming with pride.

Name _____

Judge for Yourself continued

Complete this Judgments Chart for the story "The Singing Cubs."

Event	Response	Judgment
All talent show performers must hand in their homework early.		
Bobby's mom gets sick.		
Ralphie cannot participate unless he cleans his room.		
Bobby and Megan need some help on their book reports.		
The principal realizes how hard the children have been working to be in the talent show.		

Name _____

Musical Changes

Make music of your own by joining the words and endings. Write only one letter on each line. Remember, when a base word ends with *y*, change the *y* to *i* before adding *-es*, *-er*, *-ed*, or *-est*.

1. noisy + er

_ _ _ _ _ _ _
      7

2. marry + ed

_ _ _ _ _ _
       8

3. story + es

_ _ _ _ _ _
      4

4. hungry + er

_ _ _ _ _ _ _
6

5. country + es

_ _ _ _ _ _ _ _ _
9

6. early + est

_ _ _ _ _ _ _
     3 1

7. family + es

_ _ _ _ _ _ _ _
     5

8. worry + ed

_ _ _ _ _ _
  2

Solve the riddle by writing each numbered letter on the line with the matching number.

Riddle: What kind of music do shoes like to listen to?

_ _ _ _ _ _ _ _ _
1 2 3 4   5 6 7 8 9

Name _____

Changing Final *y* to *i*

If a word ends with a consonant and *y*, change the *y* to *i* when adding *-es*, *-ed*, *-er*, or *-est*.

city + es = cit**ies**   study + ed = stud**ied**

sunny + er = sunn**ier**   heavy + est = heav**iest**

Write each Spelling Word under its ending.

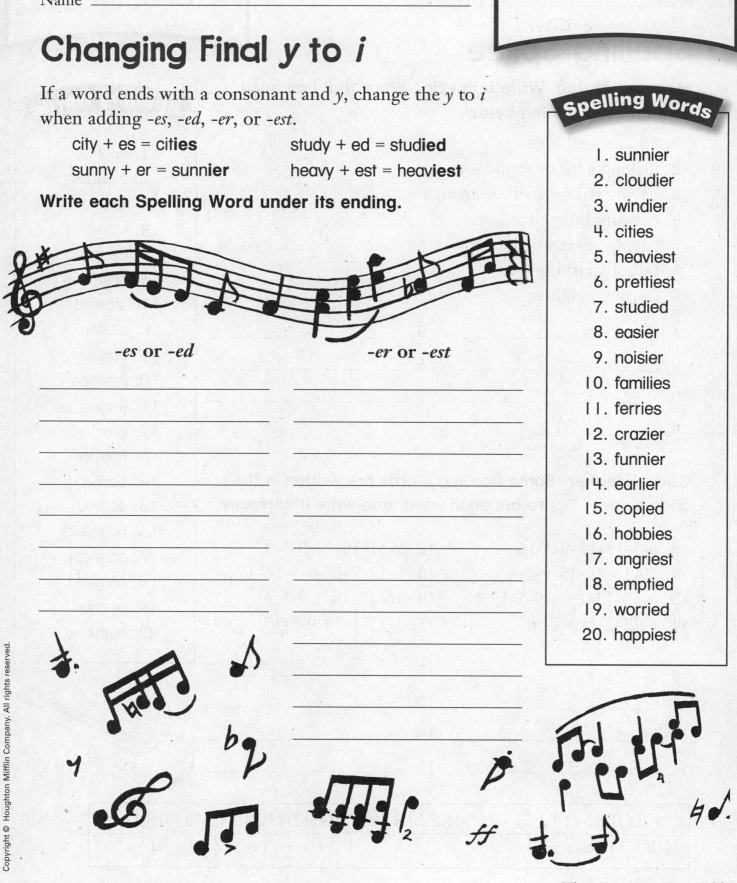

-es or -ed

_____
_____
_____
_____
_____
_____
_____

-er or -est

_____
_____
_____
_____
_____
_____
_____
_____
_____

Spelling Words

1. sunnier
2. cloudier
3. windier
4. cities
5. heaviest
6. prettiest
7. studied
8. easier
9. noisier
10. families
11. ferries
12. crazier
13. funnier
14. earlier
15. copied
16. hobbies
17. angriest
18. emptied
19. worried
20. happiest

Name _____

Spelling Spree

Meaning Match Write a Spelling Word that has each meaning and ending below.

1. do like + ed
2. making a lot of sound + er
3. having strong air movement + er
4. needing little effort + er
5. having great weight + est
6. full of sunshine + er
7. causing laughter + er

1 _____   5. _____

2. _____   6. _____

3. _____   7. _____

4. _____

Code Breaker Some Spelling Words are written in the code below. Figure out each word, and write it correctly.

8. 6-5-15-15-9-5-16   12. 5-11-14-17-9-5-4
9. 19-13-15-15-9-5-4   13. 1-12-7-15-9-5-16-17
10. 3-10-13-18-4-9-5-15   14. 16-17-18-4-9-5-4
11. 8-13-2-2-9-5-16   15. 3-15-1-20-9-5-15

8. _____   12. _____

9. _____   13. _____

10. _____   14. _____

11. _____   15. _____

CODE:	1	2	3	4	5	6	7	8	9	10	11	12	13	14	15	16	17	18	19	20
LETTER:	a	b	c	d	e	f	g	h	i	l	m	n	o	p	r	s	t	u	w	z

Spelling Words

1. sunnier
2. cloudier
3. windier
4. cities
5. heaviest
6. prettiest
7. studied
8. easier
9. noisier
10. families
11. ferries
12. crazier
13. funnier
14. earlier
15. copied
16. hobbies
17. angriest
18. emptied
19. worried
20. happiest

Name _____

Proofreading and Writing

Proofreading Circle the five misspelled Spelling Words in this poster ad. Then write each word correctly.

ONE SHOW ONLY

SUNDAY 8 PM

COMING SOON!

Are you worried about what to do Sunday night? Well, make up your mind earlyer rather than later. These tickets are going FAST! At 8 P.M., Gloria Estefan and the Miami Sound Machine will be here at the Music Hall. Imagine that! Of all the citties the group could have visited, they chose ours! Come hear some of the prittiest music you've ever heard. Bring your famlies, too! You'll be the hapiest fans around!

DON'T MISS IT!

1. _____   4. _____

2. _____   5. _____

3. _____

Spelling Words

1. sunnier
2. cloudier
3. windier
4. cities
5. heaviest
6. prettiest
7. studied
8. easier
9. noisier
10. families
11. ferries
12. crazier
13. funnier
14. earlier
15. copied
16. hobbies
17. angriest
18. emptied
19. worried
20. happiest

✏️ **Write Interview Questions** If you could interview Gloria Estefan, what questions would you ask her? Would you want to know more about her childhood? Would you ask why she chose to be a musician?

On a separate piece of paper, write a list of interview questions to ask Gloria Estefan. Use Spelling Words from the list.

Name _____

Sounds Like

Have you ever used a spelling checker on a computer? Then you know that it cannot tell the difference between two homophones.

Help Rosa by proofreading her letter to her aunt. Write the correct word from each pair on the line. The first one has been done for you.

Dear Tía Lara,

(Your You're) __You're__ not going to believe this, but I finally (won one)

_____ something! You (no know) _____ that I

       1   2

like to play basketball. Well, (there they're) _____ was a

                                           3

contest to see who could get the most baskets in three minutes.

I (threw through) _____ more than anyone. I (new knew)

                          4

_____ I had a good chance of winning. I practiced for

    5

(hours ours) _____ the week before. The (whole hole)

                6

_____ fourth grade took part, even the teachers. Our

    7

teacher, Mr. Barnes, (beet beat) _____ all the others.

                              8

The coach asked if (weed we'd) _____ like to do it again,

                                  9

and everyone said yes. So just (weight wait) _____

                                                   10

until next month!

                                          Love,
                                          Rosa

Name _____

Writing with Object Pronouns

Complete the following paragraph by writing the correct pronoun to replace the noun in parentheses. Be careful! Some of the pronouns are subjects. Use the lines provided.

When Gloria's father went to Cuba, (her father) _____
was away for two years. Gloria and her mother did not know that
(Gloria and her mother) _____ would be alone so long.
Although Gloria did not speak English, she learned (English)
_____ quickly. After her father came back from Cuba, (her
father) _____ joined the U.S. Army. Her father became ill, and
Gloria took care of (her father) _____. She listened to many
songs and learned to sing (the songs) _____. Gloria wanted to
be a professional singer but wasn't sure that (Gloria) _____
could sing well enough. At first, singing with a band was a weekend
job for (Gloria) _____. Gloria was singing but still made time
for her school courses. She did not want to neglect (the courses)
_____. Gloria and Emilio decided that (Gloria and Emilio)
_____ wanted to make music a full-time career.

Name _____

Object Pronouns

Emilio hired five workers to help him get ready for recording
sessions at a studio. You are one of them! Fill in the schedule
by writing your name on the line next to every *. Then use the
schedule to answer each question with a complete sentence.

	Monday	**Tuesday**	**Friday**
6:00 A.M. Set up instruments	* _____ Enrique	Helene * _____	* _____ Teisha
8:00 A.M. Tune guitars	* _____ Enrique	Helene Teisha	* _____ Helene
5:00 P.M. Pack up audio	Helene Teisha	* _____ Helene	* _____ Enrique
7:00 P.M. Pack instruments	* _____ Lynn	Enrique Helene	Lynn Teisha

1. If no one arrives Monday at 6:00 A.M., whom should Emilio call?

   _____

2. Who is supposed to pack up instruments on Monday?

   _____

3. Who is supposed to pack up the audio at 5:00 on Tuesday
   evening?

   _____

4. Emilio gives a key to the workers who set the instruments up.
   To whom should he give the key Friday morning?

   _____

5. E-mail messages are always sent to the workers who tune the
   guitars. To whom will they be sent on Friday?

   _____

Name _____

Using Correct Pronouns

Letty and her friends belong to a music club at school. One day they were having a discussion about their favorite Latin CDs. Read the paragraph to find out which of Gloria Estefan's albums they like best. You will have to choose and write in the correct pronouns in the sentences, so read carefully.

Letty said that (her, she) _____ likes Gloria

Estefan's songs and knows (they, them) _____ all

by heart. Ricardo thinks the Miami Sound Machine is

one of the best bands that (he, him) _____ has

ever heard. Alicia says that even the group's earliest hits

are favorites with (she, her) _____. Alicia likes

"Dr. Beat" because (they, it) _____ has a Latin

style but is in English. Letty has two favorite songs, and

(they, them) _____ are in English too. Letty says

that *Eyes of Innocence* is special for (she, her) _____.

(We, Us) _____ all like Jonathan's collection

because (he, him) _____ has a lot of Latin albums.

Jonathan met Gloria at a concert and told (we, us)

_____ about the performance.

Name _____

Problem/Solution Paragraph

Use this graphic organizer to plan your problem-solution paragraph. Write about a problem you faced at school or at home, or about a problem you might face in the future. Tell about the pros and cons of possible solutions. Then tell what solution you decided on.

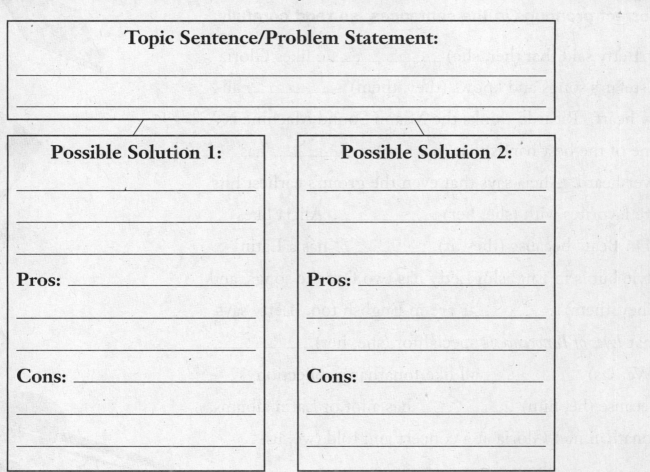

Topic Sentence/Problem Statement:

_____

_____

Possible Solution 1:	**Possible Solution 2:**
_____	_____
_____	_____
_____	_____
Pros: _____	Pros: _____
_____	_____
_____	_____
Cons: _____	Cons: _____
_____	_____
_____	_____

Concluding Sentence/Problem Solution Statement:

_____

_____

Name _____

Combining with Pronouns

Writers avoid repeating the same noun over and over by replacing it with a pronoun.

Two sentences: The name of Emilio's band was **the Miami Latin Boys.**
The Miami Latin Boys soon changed the name.

One sentence: The name of Emilio's band was **the Miami Latin Boys,** but **they** soon changed the name.

Read each pair of sentences. Combine them by replacing a noun with a pronoun in the second sentence. You may need to add or delete some words from the sentences when you combine them.

1. Gloria got good grades in school. Gloria made the honor roll.

_____

_____

2. The band played gigs on weekends. School vacations gave the band a chance to play too.

_____

_____

3. Mrs. Fajardo was a kindergarten teacher in Cuba. Mrs. Fajardo had to go back to school to get her American teaching degree.

_____

_____

4. Gloria's father had multiple sclerosis. Gloria had to give Gloria's father constant care.

_____

_____

5. Gloria loved singing. Singing became her profession.

_____

Name _____

Baseball Scramble

Unscramble the vocabulary words. Then unscramble the circled letters to solve the riddle.

Vocabulary

consecutive
fielding
first baseman
honor
modest
shortstop
sportsmanship

SUTINECCOVE

__ __ __ __ __ (O) __ (O) __ __ __

Hint: means "following one right after the other"

ROHON (O) __ __ __ __

Hint: means "to show special respect for"

SPOSTRANPIMSH

__ __ __ __ __ __ __ (O) __ __ __ __ __ __

Hint: means "quality of someone who acts with dignity in difficult situations"

NEDILFIG __ __ __ (O) __ __ __ __

Hint: means "to catch, stop, or pick up a baseball in play and throw it to the correct player"

SMOEDT __ __ __ (O) __ __

Hint: means "having a quiet, humble view of oneself"

FRITS SEMBANA

__ __ __ __ __ (O)(O) __ __ __ __ __

Hint: means "the person who plays the position around first base"

SPOTTROSH __ (O) __ (O) __ __ __ __ __

Hint: means "the position in baseball between second and third bases"

What did the pitcher do?

__ __ __ __ W __ __ __ __ I __

Name _____

Fact and Opinion Chart

Statement	Fact or Opinion	How Can You Tell? Explain.
page 585 _____ _____	Fact	_____ _____
page 586 _____ _____	Fact	_____ _____
page 589 _____ _____	Opinion	_____ _____
page 590 _____ _____	Fact	_____ _____
page 594 _____ _____	Opinion	_____ _____
page 597 _____ _____	Opinion	_____ _____
page 598 _____ _____	Fact	_____ _____

Name _____

Lou Hits a Home Run

Start at home plate and round the bases. Add words to complete each sentence that tells about an important event in Lou Gehrig's life.

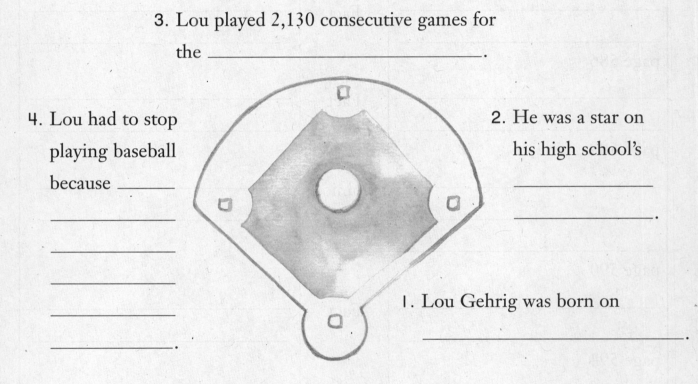

3. Lou played 2,130 consecutive games for

the _____.

4. Lou had to stop playing baseball because _____

_____

_____

_____

_____.

2. He was a star on his high school's

_____

_____.

1. Lou Gehrig was born on

_____.

5. Lou was inducted into the _____

_____

in December 1939 and is remembered for

his _____

_____.

Name _____

Check Your Facts

Read the story. Then complete the chart on the following page.

A Hero for All Seasons

Roberto Clemente is the greatest baseball player of all time. He had an incredible batting average—above .300 twelve out of the eighteen seasons he played. Having won four batting titles, twelve Gold Glove awards, and a Most Valuable Player award, he is certainly the best that ever played.

Besides being the best baseball player, Roberto Clemente was also a great man and a hero. In 1972, there was an earthquake in Nicaragua. On December 31 of that year, Clemente flew to Nicaragua to take supplies to the people. Almost immediately after takeoff, the plane crashed into the Caribbean Sea.

The best honors for Clemente came after he died. He was the first Latino voted into the Baseball Hall of Fame. In 1999, the city of Pittsburgh, where he played baseball, renamed a bridge after him—a bridge that leads to the city's beautiful new stadium.

No one summed up the life of Roberto Clemente as well as the baseball commissioner when, at Clemente's Hall of Fame award ceremony, he said, "He was so very great a man, as a leader and humanitarian, so very great an inspiration to the young and to all in baseball, especially to the proud people of his homeland, Puerto Rico." The commissioner further honored Clemente by creating a sportsmanship award in his name.

Name _____

Check Your Facts continued

Complete the chart below with facts and opinions from the story "A Hero for All Seasons."

Facts	Opinions

Name _____

Syllable Scores

As you read each sentence, pay careful attention to the underlined words. If the first vowel in a word has a long sound, circle the word. If the first vowel has a short sound, put a box around the word.

1. Lou Gehrig was a baseball player with amazing <u>talent</u>.

2. He was twice <u>chosen</u> as the American League's MVP.

3. Gehrig was a real <u>hero</u> because of the way he acted.

4. No matter how great he was, he was always a <u>modest</u> person.

5. When Gehrig stopped playing baseball, many people wanted to <u>honor</u> him.

6. It was only <u>proper</u> that Lou Gehrig know how people cared about him.

7. Thousands of fans wanted to say their <u>final</u> good-byes to Lou Gehrig.

8. No Yankee will ever again wear the number 4 on his <u>uniform</u>.

9. Lou Gehrig was <u>visibly</u> moved by the way the fans acted.

10. There will <u>never</u> be another baseball player quite like Lou Gehrig.

Count the number of words in boxes and enter the number in the box. Count the number of words in circles and enter the number in the circle below. Which team won?

	Hits	Runs
Home Team	10	▭
Visitors	7	◯

Name _____

VCV Pattern

Divide a VCV word into syllables before the consonant if the first vowel sound is long or if the first syllable ends with a vowel sound. Divide a VCV word into syllables after the consonant if the first syllable has a short vowel sound followed by a consonant sound.

V|CV: **pi | lot**   VC|V: **vis | it**

Write each Spelling Word under the heading that tells where its syllables are divided.

Spelling Words

1. pilot
2. depend
3. visit
4. human
5. seven
6. chosen
7. paper
8. reason
9. become
10. parent
11. never
12. modern
13. tiny
14. tuna
15. event
16. fever
17. moment
18. prison
19. basic
20. open

V|CV

_____   _____
_____   _____
_____   _____
_____   _____
_____   _____
_____   _____

VC|V

_____   _____
_____   _____
_____   _____

Name _____

Spelling Spree

Hidden Words Write the Spelling Word that you find in each row of letters. Don't let the other words fool you!

Example: s k i o r a n g e p   *orange*

1. e a t u n a b i   _____

2. o r p r i s o n e t   _____

3. s t o p v i s i t r n   _____

4. p o s h u m a n d   _____

5. w o n e v e n t h   _____

6. i r k r e a s o n e   _____

7. b u s e v e n c e   _____

8. r i p a r e n t i c   _____

9. t o p e n i t h   _____

10. t i n e v e r e s   _____

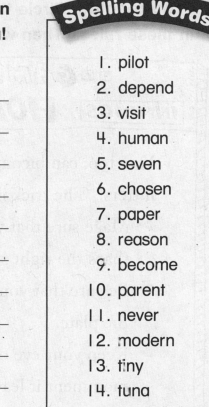

1. pilot
2. depend
3. visit
4. human
5. seven
6. chosen
7. paper
8. reason
9. become
10. parent
11. never
12. modern
13. tiny
14. tuna
15. event
16. fever
17. moment
18. prison
19. basic
20. open

Syllable Match Match the syllables at the top with the numbered syllables to write Spelling Words.

mod   lot   ti   ver   pa

11. per   12. ern   13. pi   14. ny   15. fe

11. _____   14. _____

12. _____   15. _____

13. _____

Name _____

Proofreading and Writing

Proofreading Circle the five misspelled Spelling Words in these rules. Then write each word correctly.

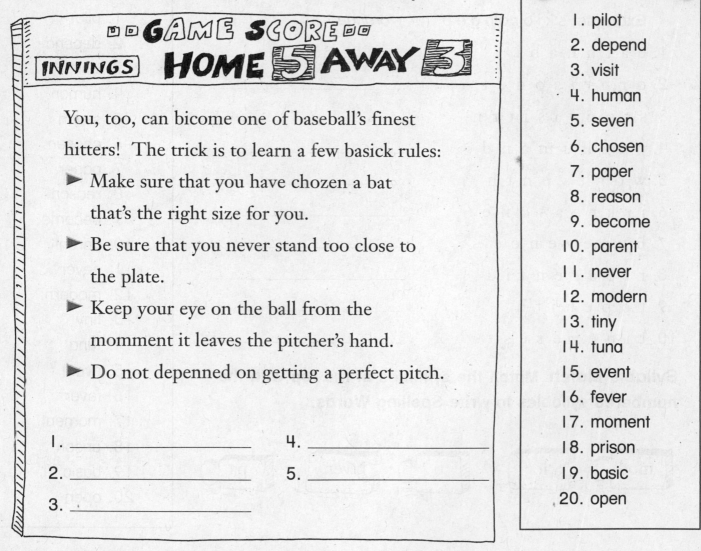

GAME SCORE
INNINGS **HOME 5 AWAY 3**

You, too, can bicome one of baseball's finest hitters! The trick is to learn a few basick rules:

► Make sure that you have chozen a bat that's the right size for you.

► Be sure that you never stand too close to the plate.

► Keep your eye on the ball from the momment it leaves the pitcher's hand.

► Do not depenned on getting a perfect pitch.

1. _____   4. _____

2. _____   5. _____

3. _____

✏️ **Write an Opinion** An **opinion** tells how you think or feel about something. For example, you might think that baseball is an exciting sport. On the other hand, you might feel that baseball is a slow, dull game.

On a separate piece of paper, write your opinion about a popular sport or game. Give reasons to back up your opinion. Use Spelling Words from the list.

Name _____

History of Base and Ball

Baseball is made up of two words, *base* and *ball*.

Read the sentences below. Write the number of the definition that shares the same word history as the underlined word or words.

base¹ *noun* **1.** The lowest part; bottom. **2.** A part used for support. **3.** The main part of something. **4.** One of the four corners of a baseball diamond. [Middle English, from Old French, from Latin *basis*, from Greek]

base² *adjective* **1.** Not honorable; shameful. **2.** Not of great value. [Middle English *bas*, low, from Old French, from Medieval Latin *bassus*]

ball¹ *noun* **1.** Something that is round. **2.** A round object used in a game or sport. **3.** A game, especially baseball, that is played with a ball. **4.** A baseball pitch that is not swung at by the batter and not thrown over home plate between the batter's knees and shoulders. [Middle English *bal*, probably from Old English *beall*]

ball² *noun* A formal social dance. [French *bal*, from Old French, from *baller*, to dance, from Late Latin *ballāre*, from Greek *ballizein*]

1. Our <u>basement</u> flooded during the storm.

_____

2. The <u>base</u> word of hitter is hit. _____

3. She goes to <u>ballet</u> class every Saturday.

_____

4. The <u>wedding</u> was held in a large ballroom.

_____

5. Everyone in the <u>ballpark</u> cheered after the home run.

_____

Name _____

Announcements with Possessives

**Finish the baseball stadium announcer's greeting by completing
the sentences with possessive pronouns.**

Good afternoon, ladies and gentlemen. The Centerville
Bombers are playing _____ fiftieth game of the season
today. The players and the management hope you will enjoy
_____ afternoon at the ballpark. We in the booth will do
_____ best to make sure you do. Brenda Jones, the
manager, has _____ work cut out for her. Larraine
Gillespie at first base has hurt _____ foot. The center
fielder and right fielder have misplaced _____ sunglasses.
We hope they catch the fly balls out there. The pitcher thinks that
the mitt she is using may not be _____. Carl Staub, the
catcher, is now pulling on _____ face mask. We hope you
have _____ scorecards ready. We have _____.

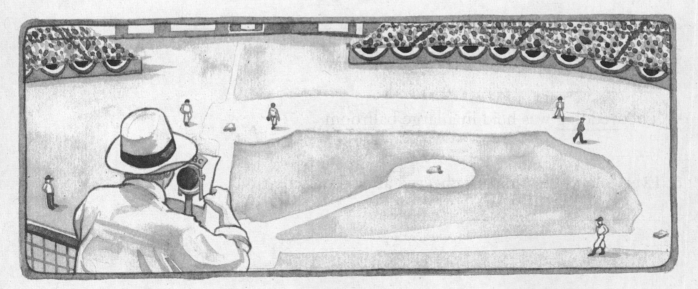

Name _____

Play Ball!

Here is a baseball game you can play. Fill in the missing possessive pronouns for the players in their positions on the field.

The center fielder knows the next job at bat will be _____ .

The left fielder is checking _____ mitt.

The second-base player moves to _____ left.

The first-base player looks at the pitcher and tosses the ball to _____ right.

The third-base player says the error was _____ .

The pitcher thinks, "_____ arm is still good."

The manager tells a player, "You will get _____ time to bat."

The catcher and pitcher almost get _____ signals mixed.

Name _____

Watching Your *its* and *it's*

Good writers are careful to use the possessive pronoun *its* and the contraction *it's* correctly in sentences.

Read the paragraph below. On the blank lines, write either *its* or *it's*, depending on which is correct. Then rewrite the paragraph correctly on the lines provided.

_____ no secret that Lou Gehrig was one of the Yankees' best players. The team moved _____ home from Baltimore to New York in 1903. Some people say of 1903, "_____ a fateful year." _____ the same year in which Lou Gehrig was born. Even when he was younger, Lou was a talented player. _____ significant that playing on his high school baseball team, he was one of _____ stars. When Lou went to Columbia University, he was a good player on _____ baseball team, too. In one of the games there, a Yankee scout saw him play. _____ a fact of history that the Yankees signed him soon afterward.

_____

_____

_____

_____

_____

_____

_____

_____

Name _____

Planning a Magazine Article

Use this organizer to plan a magazine article about a sports hero or other person you admire.

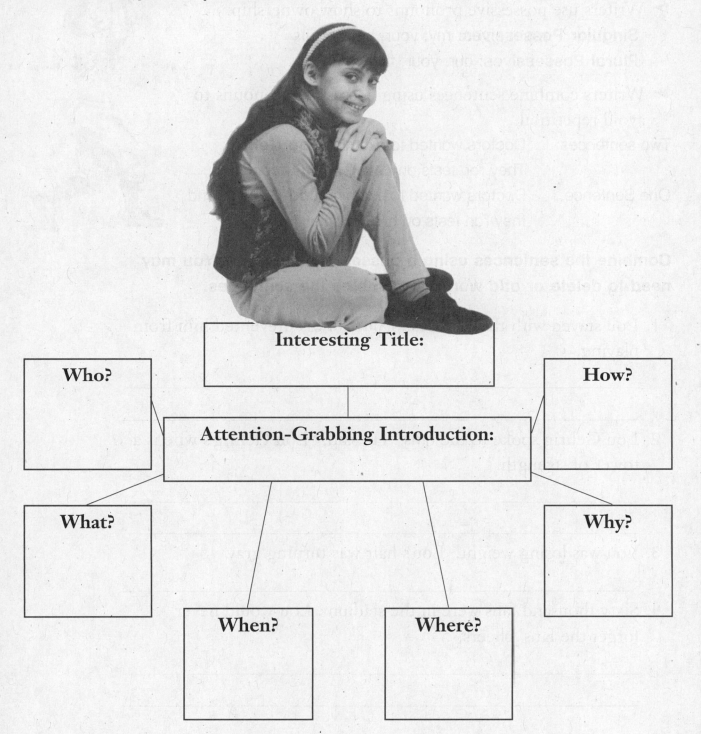

Interesting Title:

Who?

How?

Attention-Grabbing Introduction:

What?

Why?

When?

Where?

Name _____

Using Possessive Pronouns

Good writers combine sentences using possessive pronouns to improve their sentence.

► Writers use possessive pronouns to show ownership.

Singular Possessives: my, your, his, her, its

Plural Possessives: our, your, their

► Writers combine sentences using possessive pronouns to avoid repetition.

Two sentences: Doctors wanted to examine **Lou Gehrig**.
                  They ran tests on **Lou Gehrig's** condition.

One Sentence: Doctors wanted to examine **Lou Gehrig**, and
                  they ran tests on **his** condition.

Combine the sentences using a possessive pronoun. You may need to delete or add words to combine the sentences.

1. Lou stayed with the Yankees. Lou's illness prevented him from playing.

   _____

   _____

2. Lou Gehrig spoke to the fans. He said, "Lou Gehrig's wife is a tower of strength."

   _____

   _____

3. Lou was losing weight. Lou's hair was turning gray.

   _____

4. Sixty thousand fans were in the stadium. Lou would never forget the fans' cheers.

   _____

   _____

Horses and Hurricanes

Answer the questions below with a vocabulary word from the box.

Vocabulary

rocking bed
respirator
generator
admiration
foal
endangered

1. If a man needed something to sleep in that would help him breathe during the night, what might a doctor tell him to use? _____

2. Which word is the term for a young horse?

_____

3. If you are filled with wonder and amazement at an act of courage, which word describes your feelings?

_____

4. Which word describes a town put in harm's way during a terrible hurricane? _____

5. Which word means "a device that helps someone breathe"?

_____

6. What is a machine that produces power called?

_____

Cause-and-Effect Chart

Fill in the blank causes and effects in the chart below.

Stormy, Misty's Foal

Cause	Effect
A huge hurricane has hit the town of Chincoteague.	
	Mr. Terry's rocking bed has to be operated by hand.

Sacagawea

Cause	Effect
	Charbonneau panics and almost capsizes the boat.
Sacagawea finds fruits and vegetables for the Corps of Discovery to eat.	

Name _____

Making Judgments Chart

Paul in *Stormy, Misty's Foal* and Jamal in *Happy Birthday,*
Dr. King! both give something important to their communities.
Compare their actions, using the chart below.

	Paul	Jamal
What challenge does he face?		
How does he meet this challenge?		
What does he give his community?		
What might have happened if he had acted differently?		

Name _____

The Expedition

Fill in the blank with the vocabulary word that is closest in meaning to each word or phrase.

1. a kind of boat _____

2. tools _____

3. disease that makes the gums bleed

   _____

4. group with a job to do _____

5. sudden windstorm _____

6. sensible _____

> **Vocabulary**
>
> practical
> corps
> scurvy
> pirogue
> instruments
> squall
> capsizing

There is one word from the box that has not been used. Use it in a sentence below.

_____

_____

Name _____

Test Practice

Use the three steps you've learned to write an answer to both questions about *Sacagawea.* Make a chart on a separate piece of paper. Then write your answer on the lines below. Use the checklist to revise your reponse.

1. How is Sacagawea different from Charbonneau, her husband?

_____

_____

_____

_____

_____

_____

_____

_____

_____

_____

_____

_____

_____

Checklist for Writing an Answer to a Question

✔ Did I restate the question at the beginning?

✔ Can I add more details from what I read to support my answer?

✔ Do I need to delete details that do not help answer the question?

✔ Where can I add more exact words?

✔ Did I use clear handwriting? Did I make any mistakes?

Continue on page 158.

Name —————————————————————

Test Practice continued

2. **Connecting/Comparing** Gloria Estefan's family moved from Cuba to the United States when she was very young. Sacagawea left her home among the Shoshones to join the Lewis and Clark expedition. How were their experiences alike and different?

_____

_____

_____

_____

_____

_____

_____

_____

_____

_____

_____

_____

_____

Checklist for Writing an Answer to a Question

✔ Did I restate the question at the beginning?

✔ Can I add more details from what I read to support my answer?

✔ Do I need to delete details that do not help answer the question?

✔ Where can I add more exact words?

✔ Did I use clear handwriting? Did I make any mistakes?

Read both your answers aloud to a partner. Then discuss the checklist. Make any changes that will improve your answers.

Name _____

What Happened? Why Did It Happen?

Read the passage. Then answer the questions.

> The alarm clock rang. Josh slept right through the noise because he had stayed up to watch a movie the night before. When he finally got up, he was so late that he had time for only a glass of milk for breakfast. Since he was racing to catch the bus, he forgot his packed lunch. When Josh arrived at school, he was hungry. In class he thought about food so much that he couldn't finish his math problems. At lunchtime, he asked his friends for something to eat.

1. Why is Josh hungry?

_____

2. What happens because Josh stayed up to watch a movie?

_____

3. Why does Josh forget his lunch?

_____

4. Why does Josh ask his friends for food?

_____

5. Why doesn't Josh finish his math problems in class?

_____

Now write a cause-and-effect sentence about something that happened to you or that you saw today.

_____

_____

Name _____

Is It Fact? Is It Opinion?

The details below are based on stories you have read. Read each detail. Write *fact* next to each fact. Write *opinion* next to each opinion.

From *Stormy, Misty's Foal*

1. A huge storm hit the island of Chincoteague. _____

2. The town on the island was heavily damaged. _____

3. Everyone should help out in times of crisis. _____

4. Paul Beebe helped Mr. Terry by pumping the respirator. _____

5. Paul proved himself to be a hero. _____

6. As Mrs. Terry said, people who help others are wonderful. _____

From *Sacagawea*

7. In 1804 Lewis and Clark began a long journey. _____

8. Their mission was to explore and map the Louisiana Territory.

_____

9. Sacagawea was a brave young woman of the Shoshone people. _____

10. She and her husband and baby joined the expedition. _____

11. Sacagawea became one of the most important people on the journey.

_____

12. She served as interpreter and guide. _____

13. Her husband, Charbonneau, was not a good addition to the group.

_____

14. He was the worst waterman ever to paddle a pirogue. _____

15. He was an excellent trail chef, however. _____

Name _____

With and Without Endings

Write the word from the box that completes each sentence.
Then take off the ending and write the word that ends with -y.

Word Bank

silliest	parties	carried	sleepier	candies
windier	foggiest	shinier	hurried	puppies

1. The later we stayed up, the _____ we got. _____

2. My sister went to three birthday _____ in one month.

   _____

3. Florence, Oregon, is one of the _____ places I've seen.

   _____

4. We _____ through our chores so that we could play.

   _____

5. The cupcakes had cinnamon _____ on top.

   _____

6. The clown with the green hair was the _____ one at the circus.

   _____

7. Bo polished the car until it looked _____ than glass.

   _____

8. Our neighbor's collie had five _____. _____

9. It was easier to fly kites yesterday when the weather was _____.

   _____

10. We _____ the groceries into the house. _____

Name _____

Write the Right Words

Complete each sentence with a homophone. Then write your own sentences using the remaining homophones. Use a dictionary if you need help with meanings.

way / weigh / whey

1. Little Miss Muffet sat on a tuffet eating her curds and _____.

2. _____

3. _____

oar / or / ore

4. An empty rowboat with one _____ was swept along by the flood.

5. Gold _____ was discovered in California in 1848.

6. _____

road / rode / rowed

7. Lewis and Clark's men _____ the sinking pirogue to shore.

8. The girls _____ horses all afternoon.

9. _____

Name _____

Spelling Review

Write Spelling Words from the list on this page to answer the questions.

1–10. Which ten words have prefixes (*re-*, *dis-*, or *un-*) or suffixes (*-ment*, *-ful*, or *-less*)?

1. _____   6. _____

2. _____   7. _____

3. _____   8. _____

4. _____   9. _____

5. _____   10. _____

11–20. Which ten words have a base word that changes the final *y* to *i* when an ending is added?

11. _____   16. _____

12. _____   17. _____

13. _____   18. _____

14. _____   19. _____

15. _____   20. _____

21–30. Write the ten words with the VCV pattern that do not have prefixes, suffixes, or endings. Then draw a line between each syllable.

21. _____   26. _____

22. _____   27. _____

23. _____   28. _____

24. _____   29. _____

25. _____   30. _____

Spelling Words

1. parent
2. angriest
3. fever
4. powerful
5. visit
6. unsure
7. families
8. seven
9. crazier
10. displease
11. tuna
12. redo
13. kindness
14. cities
15. dislike
16. easier
17. never
18. paper
19. movement
20. reread
21. happiest
22. prison
23. become
24. peaceful
25. studied
26. reason
27. copied
28. earlier
29. useless
30. worried

Name _____

Spelling Spree

Crossword Puzzle Write a Spelling Word in the puzzle that means the same as each clue.

Across

1. not *warlike* but _____
3. I study now. You _____ yesterday.
5. one, three, five, _____, nine
7. happy, happier, _____

Down

1. pencil and _____
2. towns and _____
4. the opposite of *like*
6. not *later* but _____

Spelling Words

1. movement
2. happiest
3. seven
4. earlier
5. dislike
6. cities
7. powerful
8. paper
9. tuna
10. prison
11. worried
12. angriest
13. peaceful
14. parent
15. studied

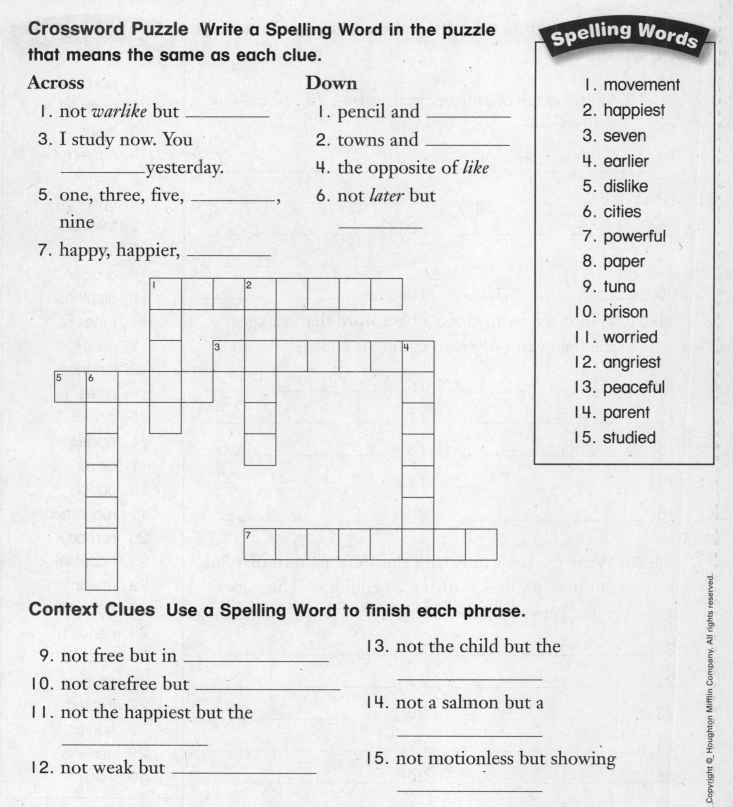

Context Clues Use a Spelling Word to finish each phrase.

9. not free but in _____
10. not carefree but _____
11. not the happiest but the _____
12. not weak but _____

13. not the child but the _____
14. not a salmon but a _____
15. not motionless but showing _____

Name _____

Proofreading and Writing

Proofreading Circle the six misspelled Spelling Words in this essay. Then write each word correctly.

When we rereed stories about heroes, we find that they almost nevur attempt useles tasks. They often come from familys where honesty is important. Sometimes they are shown much kindnes by others. Sometimes they are unshur of themselves.

1. _____ 4. _____

2. _____ 5. _____

3. _____ 6. _____

Spelling Words

1. redo
2. reread
3. unsure
4. useless
5. displease
6. kindness
7. easier
8. families
9. copied
10. crazier
11. visit
12. reason
13. become
14. never
15. fever

Description of a Hero Write Spelling Words to complete this description.

Every day Mrs. Mendez goes to 7. _____ a family nearby. The 8. _____ she does this is to help them. One day the family's baby had a high 9. _____. The parents kept getting 10. _____ with worry, but they didn't have a car. Mrs. Mendez took them to the doctor in her car, which was much 11. _____ and faster than riding the bus. Some neighbors have 12. _____ Mrs. Mendez's idea and are helping others. I hope to 13. _____ a neighborhood hero like Mrs. Mendez! Her actions never 14. _____ anyone. First, I will help my sister 15. _____ her homework.

✏️ **Write a Letter** On a separate sheet of paper, write a letter to a friend about a hero you admire. Use the Spelling Review Words.

Name _____

Writing Subject Pronouns

For each sentence below, write a subject pronoun to replace the word or words given in parentheses. Write your sentence on the lines provided.

1. (A hurricane) had flooded the town.

_____

2. (Many people) could not get supplies.

_____

3. (The boat driver) gave a task to Paul.

_____

4. (The Terrys) had very little gasoline for Mr. Terry's rocking bed.

_____

5. (The bed) had to be rocked twenty-eight times a minute.

_____

6. (Paul) had to rock the bed by hand.

_____

7. (Mrs. Terry) announced the arrival of gasoline for the rocking bed.

_____

8. (Mr. Terry) and (Mrs. Terry) thanked Paul for his hard work.

_____

Name _____

Using Object Pronouns in Sentences

Complete the following paragraph by writing the correct pronoun to replace the noun in parentheses. Some of the pronouns are objects, and some are subjects. Use the lines provided.

Our family received a telephone call from (some neighbors)

_____. They warned (my parents and me)

_____ about a possible flood. (My parents and I)

_____ looked out at the river. My father asked (my

mother) _____ for two suitcases. (My mother)

_____ pulled them quickly from the closet. (My

father) _____ gave some papers to (my mother)

_____. She put (the papers) _____ in

one suitcase, along with our family albums. (My parents)

_____ filled the other suitcase with clothes. We put

(the suitcases) _____ into our car and drove to a

safe area.

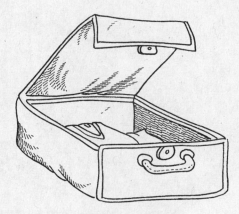

Name _____

Words About Tales

Choose the word from the Vocabulary box that best completes each sentence.

1. Courage and curiosity are two

   _____ that a person might have.

2. It is fun to be around someone with a cheerful

   _____.

3. Lighting candles and singing "Happy Birthday"

   are two birthday _____.

4. Talking animals and silly situations are often

   found in _____.

5. "Long, long ago, when the world was young" is a beginning to

   a _____ tale.

Vocabulary

customs
folktales
personality
traditional
traits

Answer this question with one sentence. Use three words from the Vocabulary box in your sentence.

What kinds of stories often describe people's ways of life?

6. _____

_____

_____

Name _____

Pourquoi Tales Chart

	"Why the Sun and the Moon Live in the Sky"	"Tiger"
At the start of the tale, the main characters are unusual in some way.		
A problem or goal gets the tale going.		
Main events follow.		
The tale ends.		
The tale explains why . . .		

Name _____

Talking About Tales

Compare and contrast two of the pourquoi tales you just read by completing the chart below.

	Story #1	Story #2
	_____ (title)	_____ (title)
How are the characters the same and different?		
How are the problem and the solution the same and different?		
How is the language the same and different?		

Now tell which pourquoi tale is your favorite and why.

_____

_____

_____

Name _____

Believe It or Not!

You are a news reporter for a local television station. Your program is called "Believe It or Not!" You have just found a very large turtle sleeping in the mud during winter. How will you explain it to your viewers? Tell them a pourquoi tale.

Write notes for your tale below. Also, write questions you could ask the people — and the animals — on the scene.

Name _____

Elements of a Pourquoi Tale

Fill out the chart for the tale "How Turtle Flew South for the Winter."

	"How Turtle Flew South for the Winter"
At the start of the tale, the main characters are unusual in some way.	
A problem or goal gets the tale going.	
Main events follow.	
The tale ends.	
The tale explains why . . .	

Write a paragraph to answer this question. Include details from the tale to support your answer.

In what ways does Turtle seem like a person?

_____

_____

_____

_____

Name _____

Syllable Pairs

**Read each clue. Find the pair of syllables in the box that can be
put together to make the word that matches the clue. Write the
word with a line between the syllables.**

nus	id	si	in	ture	al	nis	fu	par	splen
med	cant	rap	bo	va	lent	don	nus	did	cab

1. to forgive _____

2. the opposite of noisy _____

3. a synonym for *fast* _____

4. something extra _____

5. an award to wear _____

6. a synonym for *empty* _____

7. beautifully bright _____

8. a house of logs _____

9. a game with a net _____

10. time that has not happened yet _____

Name _____

More VCV Pattern

Divide a VCV word before the consonant if the first vowel sound is long or has the schwa sound. Divide the word after the consonant if the first syllable has a short vowel sound followed by a consonant sound.

v l c v	vc l v
t i l g e r	c l e v l e r
b e l l o n g	

Write each Spelling Word under the heading that shows where the word is divided into syllables. Draw a line between the syllables.

V l CV

VC l V

_____   _____

_____   _____

_____   _____

_____   _____

_____   _____

_____   _____

_____   _____

_____   _____

_____

_____

Spelling Words

1. tiger
2. belong
3. clever
4. wagon
5. defend
6. river
7. award
8. season
9. metal
10. palace
11. spider
12. frozen
13. figure
14. police
15. dragon
16. exit
17. decide
18. delay
19. finish
20. total

Name _____

Spelling Spree

Phrase Fillers Write the Spelling Word that best completes each phrase.

1. a _____ car's siren

2. a huge, scaly _____

3. to _____ to a club

4. to _____ a prize

5. so cold it was _____ solid

6. a _____ fit for a king or a queen

7. a "No _____" sign

8. to _____ for or against

Letter Math Add and subtract letters from the words below to write Spelling Words.

9. petal – p + m = _____

10. finger – ger + ish = _____

11. topaz– paz + tal = _____

12. depend – p + f = _____

13. cl + never - n = _____

14. dragon – dr + w = _____

15. shiver – sh + r = _____

to have a tiger by the tail

Name _____

Proofreading and Writing

Proofreading Circle the six misspelled Spelling Words in this pourquoi tale. Then write each word correctly.

Why the Spider Has a Web

One day the forest animals were decorating their home. As the tigur was finishing a poster, he dropped some glue on the ground.

Just then a spieder came along. Without looking, she stepped in the glue. As she walked away, a thin thread of glue trailed behind her and wouldn't come off. Now she had to figgur out how to use the glue.

Without dellay, she crawled off to a spot near the rivver. Then she used the sticky thread to build a place to live and to catch food. Then she settled down to wait. If you visit the woods in the right seeson, you can still see her sitting in her web.

Spelling Words

1. tiger
2. belong
3. clever
4. wagon
5. defend
6. river
7. award
8. season
9. metal
10. palace
11. spider
12. frozen
13. figure
14. police
15. dragon
16. exit
17. decide
18. delay
19. finish
20. total

1. _____ 4. _____

2. _____ 5. _____

3. _____ 6. _____

✏→ **Write a Dialogue** Suppose that the spider had asked the tiger to help her get rid of the glue. How might they have tried to solve the problem?

On a separate sheet of paper, write a dialogue between the two animals as they discuss the problem and a solution. Use Spelling Words from the list.

Name _____

Creature Features

Write the letter of the description that best matches each animal's name.

1. _____ fox   a. powerful and stubborn

2. _____ mouse   b. shy and fearful

3. _____ bull   c. fierce and greedy

4. _____ monkey   d. sly and clever

5. _____ shark   e. mischievous and playful

Answer each question. Use the underlined word in your answer.

6. Would a <u>bullheaded</u> person easily change his or her mind? Explain.

_____

7. Does someone with a <u>mousy</u> manner like attention? Explain.

_____

8. Why might someone be told, "Stop <u>monkeying</u> around"?

_____

9. If a storekeeper is known as a <u>shark</u>, should you be a customer?

_____

10. Could a thief be <u>outfoxed</u>? Why or why not?

_____

Name _____

Why Whiskers?

**Combine each pair of sentences. Use the word shown to begin
each new sentence. Then finish the story by adding your own
ideas to the last three sentences.**

1. The world was young. Cat and Mouse were friends.

   When _____

2. Mouse was sleepy. She curled up in some straw.

   Because _____

3. Cat saw the straw. She asked Mouse to move over.

   When _____

4. There was plenty of straw. Mouse would not share it.

   Although _____

5. Mouse was so greedy. Cat became angry and hissed.

   Because _____

   _____

6. When Mouse threw some straw at Cat, _____

   _____

7. When the straw hit Cat's face, it _____

8. Because Mouse threw straw at Cat, cats today

   _____

   _____

Name _____

Combining Sentences

Read this short tale. Then combine the sentences below.
Begin each combined sentence with *when, although,* or *because*.

> Long ago, all animals were the same height. Giraffe had short legs and a short neck. One day, Giraffe saw a tall tree. He wanted to eat the tasty leaves at the top. He stretched his legs, but he still couldn't reach the leaves. Then he stretched his neck. At last he could munch on the tasty top leaves.

1. Giraffe saw the tall tree. He tried to reach the top leaves.

   _____

2. Giraffe was very hungry. He stretched his legs.

   _____

3. Giraffe was closer to the leaves. He still could not reach them.

   _____

4. He stretched his legs again. He also stretched his neck.

   _____

5. Giraffe stretched very hard. He grew taller.

   _____

6. Giraffe's neck grew longer. He could reach the tops of trees.

   _____

7. Giraffes used to be short. Now they are tall.

   _____

8. Write a compound sentence about this story. _____

   _____

Name _____

Using Pronouns

Proofread this story. When a noun appears for a second time in the same sentence, replace it with a pronoun. Also correct capitalization and punctuation errors. Use proofreading marks.

Example: rain helped Earth, and Earth became happy

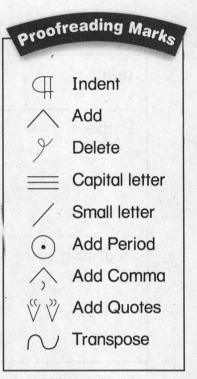

Proofreading Marks

⊓ Indent
∧ Add
⅄ Delete
≡ Capital letter
/ Small letter
⊙ Add Period
⌄ Add Comma
❝❞ Add Quotes
∽ Transpose

Earth and Rain

long ago, Rain fell up. He rose from the ground to the sky. When Rain was happy, Rain zoomed up and up

Earth was lonely? She watched Rain play in the sky. when Earth saw Rain, Earth cried.

Rain looked down and saw Earth crying. Because Rain felt sorry for Earth, Rain turned around. He fell to Earth

Earth was so happy that Earth began to sing. Earth's song woke the flowers, and the flowers bloomed.

Name _____

Planning a Pourquoi Tale

Use this chart to plan your Pourquoi Tale.

Plot	Characters
Problem	Name and description of main character
Beginning event	
Middle events	Names and descriptions of other characters
Ending	
What the tale explains	

Name _____

Stamp Out Vague Verbs!

Read each part of the story. Write an exact verb to replace the general word or phrase in parentheses. Remember that an exact verb helps readers see and hear things clearly.

1. Long, long ago, Mosquito listened as Wren (made) beautiful songs.

   _____

2. Mosquito wished he could sing high notes like Wren, but he could only (make low sounds).

   _____

3. Mosquito asked Wren for voice lessons, but Wren (said in an unkind way), "Sorry, your voice is too low. I can't work miracles."

   _____

4. Mosquito felt so insulted! He breathed in deeply. Then he let out his anger in a voice that began low but (went) higher, higher, and higher still.

   _____

5. Mosquito (moved fast) from here to there, letting out out an impossibly high, ear-splitting *mmmmm*.

   _____

6. Mosquito could never use a low voice again. He has (made a high sound) ever since.

   _____

Name _____

Nature: Friend and Foe

How can nature be a friend? How can it be a foe?

Complete the word webs with words and phrases that describe spiders and thunderstorms, both as friends and as foes.

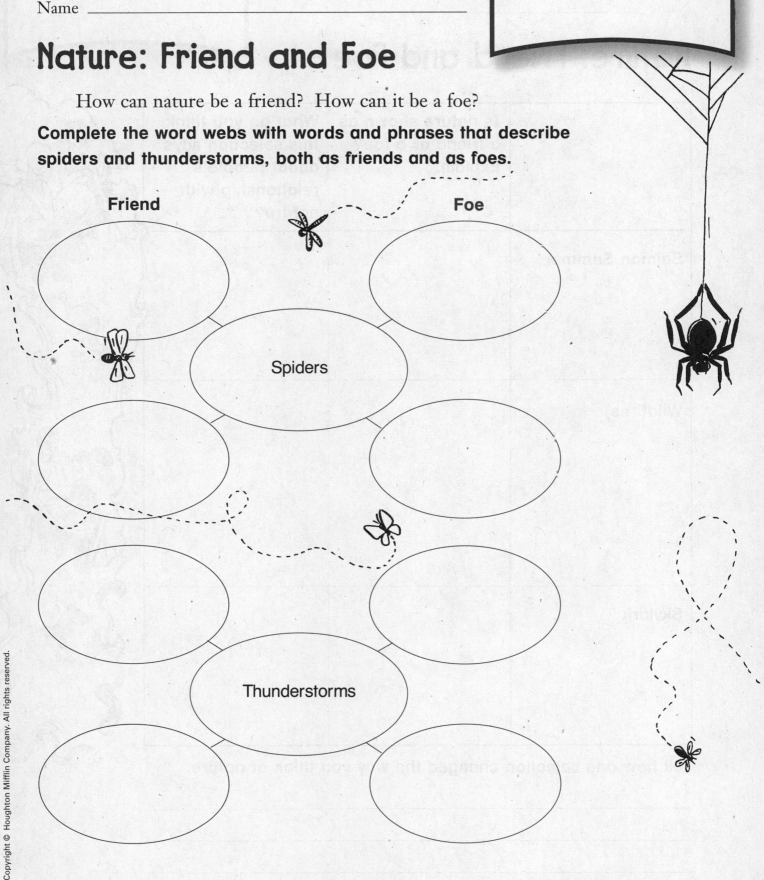

Friend

Foe

Spiders

Thunderstorms

Name _____

Nature: Friend and Foe

	Is nature shown as a friend or a foe? Explain.	What do you think this selection says about people's relationship with nature?
Salmon Summer		
Wildfires		
Skylark		

Tell how one selection changed the way you think of nature.

_____

_____

_____

Name _____

Word Riddle

Write a word from the box that answers the riddle.

1. What do you call relatives from whom you have descended? _____

2. What do you call it when fish lay eggs and reproduce in a river? _____

3. What do you call a plentiful supply of something?

   _____

4. I am the fake bait that fishermen use to attract fish. What am I?

   _____

5. I'm the name for animals that feed on dead plants and animals. What am I?

   _____

Write a sentence using two words from the box.

_____

_____

Name _____

Directions Flow Chart

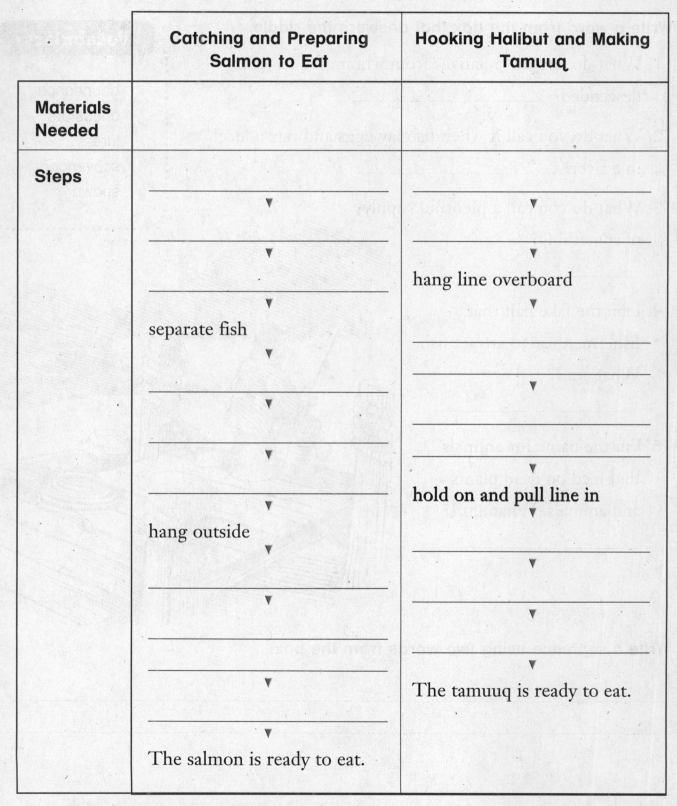

	Catching and Preparing Salmon to Eat	Hooking Halibut and Making Tamuuq
Materials Needed		
Steps		

Catching and Preparing Salmon to Eat:

_____ ▼

_____ ▼

_____ ▼

separate fish ▼

_____ ▼

_____ ▼

_____ ▼

hang outside ▼

_____ ▼

_____ ▼

_____ ▼

The salmon is ready to eat.

Hooking Halibut and Making Tamuuq:

_____ ▼

hang line overboard ▼

_____ ▼

_____ ▼

_____ ▼

hold on and pull line in ▼

_____ ▼

_____ ▼

_____ ▼

The tamuuq is ready to eat.

Name _____

Nothing But the Truth

Mark *T* if the statement is true and *F* if it is false. If the statement is false, rewrite it on a separate sheet of paper to make a true statement.

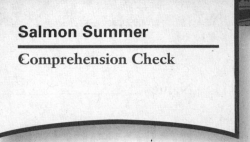

Statement	True or False?
1. Alex's favorite snack is smoked salmon.	1. _____
2. When he cleans fish for the smokehouse, Alex leaves the tails and skin on.	2. _____
3. Magpies and gulls are scavengers that eat fish scraps.	3. _____
4. Alex hangs smoked salmon in a closet to cure.	4. _____
5. Alex baits lobster traps with small salmon.	5. _____
6. When a crab is too big to keep, Alex throws it back.	6. _____
7. Alex fishes with a line and a silver lure.	7. _____
8. The fish head downstream to mate.	8. _____
9. To catch a halibut, Alex baits his hook with a salmon.	9. _____
10. To make tamuuq takes about ten hours.	10. _____

Name _____

Following Tradition

Read the story below and then answer the questions on the following page.

Thanksgiving with the Muslovs

It was the night before Thanksgiving and in the Muslov family that meant it was time to prepare the salmon. It was the way they had always celebrated, and this year was special for Leonin — he was finally old enough to help prepare the fish.

"Leo," his father called from the kitchen. "Go get the recipe box, will you?" Leonin got up from the living room floor where he was reading and quickly brought the recipe box into the kitchen. "Thank you, Leo. You ready? Okay. Read me the instructions, please."

"It says we need two to three pounds of salmon filets," Leo said carefully. "We need to place the salmon in a mixture of water, salt, sugar, garlic, and dill. The filets need to be coated with the mixture and then covered with plastic wrap. Then it says to leave them in the refrigerator overnight." Leo paused for a moment. "But Dad, we don't have any filets."

"You're right, but we do have whole salmon in the refrigerator. Your job is to cut off their heads and tails and pull out their insides. Then you have to carefully remove their bones so you're left with the biggest, most tender piece of meat. That's the filet."

It was at that moment that Leonin began to wonder why he had been so excited to help.

Name _____

Following Tradition continued

Complete the chart below and answer the questions based on "Thanksgiving with the Muslovs."

What ingredients and materials do you need?

What are the step-by-step directions for preparing the salmon?

_____

_____

_____

_____

_____

_____

Why do you think the salmon is supposed to be left in the mixture overnight? What do you think would happen if it wasn't?

_____

_____

_____

Name _____

Seaworthy Syllables

Read this description of a well-known sea animal. Write the number below each underlined word next to the word's definition. Use a dictionary if you need help. Then use the clues in the description to identify the sea animal.

This animal may <u>inhabit</u> shallow parts of the ocean or live in deep
    1
waters. It got its name because of the eight long arms sticking out of its
head. The <u>underside</u> of each arm has <u>powerful</u> sucker. These suckers
         2   3
can provide <u>enormous</u> suction to help the animal attach itself to rocks.
              4
This sea creature has two eyes, one on each side of its head. These
eyes are <u>similar</u> to the eyes of human beings. This animal has many
          5
enemies, including whales, seals, and even certain fish. To protect
itself against these <u>predators</u>, this animal hides itself by <u>discharging</u>
                      6   7
a cloud of inky fluid. It may also escape by <u>rapidly</u> changing its
                                              8
color to scare an enemy or blend with its surroundings.

_____ very large   _____ quickly

_____ releasing   _____ like

_____ live in   _____ having great strength

_____ enemies   _____ surface underneath

The name of this sea animal is: _____.

Three-Syllable Words

To spell a three-syllable word, divide the word into syllables. Remember to look for familiar spelling patterns. Pay attention to the spelling of the unstressed syllables. Spell the word by syllables.

yes | ter | day /yĕs′ tər dā/   **de | liv | er** /dĭ lĭv′ ər/

Write each Spelling Word under the heading that tells which syllable is stressed.

First Syllable Stressed

_____
_____
_____
_____
_____
_____
_____
_____
_____
_____

Second Syllable Stressed

_____
_____
_____
_____
_____
_____
_____
_____

Spelling Words

1. deliver
2. favorite
3. camera
4. yesterday
5. tomorrow
6. important
7. together
8. victory
9. remember
10. library
11. enemy
12. animal
13. another
14. however
15. banana
16. alphabet
17. hospital
18. hamburger
19. carpenter
20. several

Salmon Summer

Spelling Three-Syllable Words

Spelling Spree

Questions Write a Spelling Word to answer each question.

1. Which word names a fruit?
2. Who builds things?
3. What do you call a living organism that is not a plant?
4. What word names more than one?
5. What tastes great with ketchup?
6. Where do you go when you need an operation?
7. Where is the quietest place in town?
8. What do you need to make any word?
9. What day came just before today?
10. What word is the opposite of *friend*?

1. _____   6. _____
2. _____   7. _____
3. _____   8. _____
4. _____   9. _____
5. _____   10. _____

Word Search Write the Spelling Word that is hidden in each sentence.

Example: The troop leaders always <u>run happy</u> meetings. *unhappy*

11. Are membership forms available for the Girl Scouts?
12. I'd like to show everyone this video.
13. My mother made liver and bacon for dinner.
14. Which team was the victor yesterday?
15. The fire truck came racing down the street.

11. _____
12. _____
13. _____
14. _____
15. _____

Spelling Words

1. deliver
2. favorite
3. camera
4. yesterday
5. tomorrow
6. important
7. together
8. victory
9. remember
10. library
11. enemy
12. animal
13. another
14. however
15. banana
16. alphabet
17. hospital
18. hamburger
19. carpenter
20. several

194   Theme 6: **Nature: Friend and Foe**

Name _____

Proofreading and Writing

Proofreading Circle the five misspelled Spelling Words in this part of an e-mail message. Then write each word correctly.

IN BOX ⇕ DISPLAY | SUBJECT | DATE | NAME

To: Alex

Subject: Fishing

I'm looking forward to your return to fish camp tomorow. First, we will go out togather to pick fish from the gill net. Remember to bring your gloves. You know how importent it is to protect your hands from jellyfish stings! Then we will go fishing, and you can try to catch anuther halibut. If you are lucky, we'll make tamuuq out of it. I know that's your favorate!

Spelling Words

1. deliver
2. favorite
3. camera
4. yesterday
5. tomorrow
6. important
7. together
8. victory
9. remember
10. library
11. enemy
12. animal
13. another
14. however
15. banana
16. alphabet
17. hospital
18. hamburger
19. carpenter
20. several

1. _____   4. _____

2. _____   5. _____

3. _____

✏️ **Write Animal Facts** Alex knew a lot about salmon. He could recognize the different kinds, and he knew about the life cycle of the salmon. What animal do you know facts about?

On a separate sheet of paper, write a paragraph of information about an animal that you find interesting. Make sure to tell why you find this animal interesting. Use Spelling Words from the list.

Sensible Meanings

As you read each sentence, think about the meaning of the underlined word. Then find the numbered meaning in the box. Print that number on the line by the sentence.

1. Water mammal
2. To close tightly
3. To go separate ways
4. A role
5. To be in flight
6. Two-winged insect
7. To pay out money
8. To pass time

1. The family will <u>fly</u> from California to Alaska. ____

2. The <u>seal</u> dove into the water and caught a fish. ____

3. We always <u>spend</u> the summer at the beach. ____

4. Henry and Lou were such good friends that they hated to <u>part</u>. ____

5. Toby licked the envelope to <u>seal</u> it. ____

6. He got the <u>part</u> of the detective because of his fine acting. ____

7. Every time we open the door, another <u>fly</u> comes in. ____

8. Don't <u>spend</u> all your allowance at once. ____

Name _____

Riddles with Adverbs

**Read these riddles about the animals on Kodiak Island.
Underline the adverb in each riddle. On the line, write the
animal that the riddle is about.**

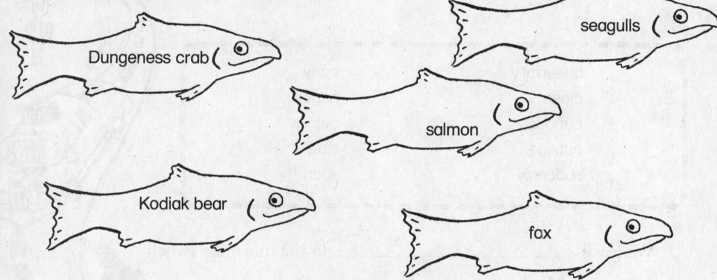

1. These animals swim alone into the river to catch their fish.

   _____

2. These fish swim upstream to spawn and die.

   _____

3. These birds swoop down to catch fish scraps.

   _____

4. This animal looks watchfully for food for her young pups.

   _____

5. This animal crawls backward on the sea bottom.

   _____

**On a separate sheet of paper, write two riddles of your own
about other things in the story. Use an adverb in each and
underline it. Draw a clue for each riddle.**

Name _____

Adverbs and Kodiak Island

The Fremson family members are taking a trip to Kodiak Island.
Complete the sentences by writing adverbs that tell how, when, or
where. The word in parentheses tells you what kind of adverb to
use.

cheerfully	early
close	happily
curiously	quickly
outside	slowly
suddenly	soon

1. We leave _____ in the morning. (when)

2. Mother and Father put their coats on

   _____. (how)

3. _____, a taxi arrives. (how)

4. The family goes _____. (where)

5. The Fremsons _____ wave goodbye

   to their neighbors. (how)

6. The taxi moves _____ down the street.

   (how)

7. Brenda _____ sings a song. (how)

8. Marcus studies the map _____. (how)

9. _____ the taxi arrives at the airport.

   (when)

10. The taxi stops _____ to the entrance.

    (where)

198   Theme 6: **Nature: Friend and Foe**

Name _____

Writing with Adverbs

Adverbs add specific details to your sentences and make them more interesting.

Read the sentences, and then choose an adverb from the list below to expand each sentence. Write your sentences on the lines.

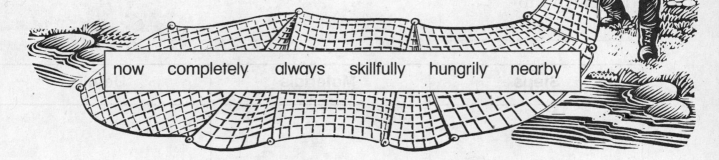

| now | completely | always | skillfully | hungrily | nearby |

1. Alex and his father fish in the neighborhood stream. (where)

   _____

2. At age nine, the boy can help his father fish with a net. (when)

   _____

3. The boy picks fish from the net. (how)

   _____

4. Alex wears gloves to protect his hands. (when)

   _____

5. Alex cuts the fish and hangs them up to dry. (how)

   _____

6. Alex and his brother Larry eat the smoked salmon. (how)

   _____

On another sheet of paper, write two of your own sentences about Alex. Use at least one adverb in each sentence. Underline the adverb.

Name _____

How-to Paragraph Planner

You can use this graphic organizer to help plan your how-to paragraph. Then write an interesting topic sentence and a closer that sums up the directions.

Topic: How to
_____

Steps	Materials	Details

Topic Sentence:
_____
_____

Closing Sentence:
_____
_____

Name _____

Order Words and Phrases

Good writers use order words and phrases to tell the sequence of steps and make instructions easy to follow.

Order words and phrases include **first, second, next, during, while, now, then, later, after that, the next step,** and **finally.**

Read each how-to paragraph. Rewrite the paragraph, adding order words or phrases.

1. Making an apple and peanut butter sandwich is easy. All you need is an apple, a knife, and a jar of peanut butter. You slice the apple into thin wedges. You spread every other apple slice with peanut butter. You put one clean slice and one peanut butter slice together to make a sandwich.

_____

_____

_____

_____

_____

2. Eli makes his own trail mix. He needs a large plastic container, raisins, peanuts, chocolate chips, and half a dried apple. He puts the raisins, peanuts, and chocolate chips into the container. He cuts up the dried apple into small pieces. He adds the apple pieces to the mix. He puts the lid on the container and shakes it up.

_____

_____

_____

_____

_____

Name _____

Revising Your Research Report

Reread your research report. Put a checkmark in the box for each sentence that describes your paper. Use this page to help you revise.

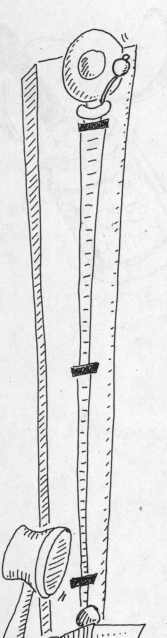

Rings the Bell

- [ ] My report is focused on a topic. It is well researched.

- [ ] Each paragraph has a topic sentence supported by facts.

- [ ] I wrote the facts in my own words. I used exact words.

- [ ] My sentences flow smoothly, and there are few mistakes.

- [ ] I wrote a strong conclusion. My list of sources is complete.

Getting Stronger

- [ ] The report could be more focused. I need more facts.

- [ ] My paragraphs need topic sentences or supporting facts.

- [ ] I didn't always use my own words, or exact words.

- [ ] Some sentences are choppy. There are a few mistakes.

- [ ] My conclusion is weak. My list of sources is incomplete.

Try Harder

- [ ] I never focus on a topic. There are almost no facts.

- [ ] My facts are not organized in paragraphs.

- [ ] I copied sentences from a source. There are no exact words.

- [ ] Most sentences are choppy. There are many mistakes.

- [ ] The conclusion is missing. I have no list of sources.

Name _____

Using Adverbs Correctly

Underline the adverb that correctly completes each sentence.

1. I love watching (quiet/quietly) as rain comes down outside.

2. I like to hear the thunder boom (loud/loudly).

3. My cat, Molly, moves (careful/carefully) across the room.

4. The thunder is (real/really) loud.

5. Molly slinks (slow/slowly) under the couch.

6. The lightning flashes (bright/brightly) in the sky.

7. The room lights up (total/totally).

8. Molly meows (sad/sadly) from under the couch.

9. I reach under the couch to pet her (gentle/gently).

10. She hisses (anger, angirly), thinking I'm the

    thunder coming to get her.

Name _____

Spelling Words

Most of the Spelling Words on the list are homophones. Homophones are words that sound alike but have different meanings and spellings. When you write a homophone, be sure to spell the word that has the meaning you want.

Write the missing letters and apostrophes in the Spelling Words below.

Spelling Words

1. their
2. there
3. they're
4. your
5. you're
6. its
7. it's
8. to
9. too
10. two
11. they
12. than
13. then
14. right
15. write

1. th ____ ____ r
2. th ____ r ____
3. th ____ ____ ____
4. y ____ ____ ____
5. you ____ ____ ____
6. it ____
7. it____ ____
8. t ____

9. t ____ ____
10. t ____ ____
11. th ____ ____
12. th ____ n
13. th ____ n
14. r ____ ____ ____ ____
15. ____ rite

Study List On a separate sheet of paper, write each Spelling Word. Check your spelling against the words on the list.

Spelling Spree

Name _____

Homophone Blanks The blanks in each of the following sentences can be filled with homophones from the Spelling Word list. Write the words in the correct order.

1. their
2. there
3. they're
4. your
5. you're
6. its
7. it's
8. to
9. too
10. two
11. they
12. than
13. then
14. right
15. write

1–3. It's _____ o'clock now, so it's probably

_____ late _____ go out for lunch.
2   3

4–5. So _____ telling me that's not _____ car?
4   5

6–7. I heard _____ unusual to see a snake during the
6

time it sheds _____ skin.
7

8–9. When you address the letter, be sure to _____
8

the _____ zip code.
9

Th- Clues Use the clues to write these *th-* Spelling Words.

10. If someone asks you the question "where?" you can use this word to answer.
11. This word is used to compare (more _____, less _____).
12. This contraction can be used to tell what others are doing.
13. This is a word for something that belongs to others.
14. This is a word you can use to talk about a group of people.
15. This word can be used to put a story in the right order.

10. _____   13. _____

11. _____   14. _____

12. _____   15. _____

Theme 6: **Nature: Friend and Foe**   205

Proofreading and Writing

Proofreading Circle the five misspelled words in this storm warning. Then write each word correctly.

The National Weather Service has issued a tornado warning for our viewing area. So far, too tornadoes have already touched down, and they're saying that more could hit before this storm passes. If you are out in you're car, try to find shelter as quickly as you can. Get off the road right now even if the sky looks okay to you—better to be safe then sorry. Do the rite thing and go somewhere safe. We'll keep you posted on this storm until its over.

Spelling Words

1. their
2. there
3. they're
4. your
5. you're
6. its
7. it's
8. to
9. too
10. two
11. they
12. than
13. then
14. right
15. write

_____

_____

_____

_____

✏️ **Write a Poem** On a separate piece of paper, write a short poem about nature in its role of friend, foe, or both. Use Spelling Words from the list.

Name _____

Fire Words

**Choose the meaning that best fits the underlined
vocabulary word as it is used in the sentence.
Write the letter of your answer on the line.**

1. Forest fires seem to occur in <u>cycles</u>. _____
   A. hilly areas   C. repeating periods of time
   B. circles   D. dry areas

2. If that liquid is <u>flammable</u>, keep it away from the fire. _____
   A. able to be set on fire   C. hot
   B. excitable   D. oily and thick

3. The burning <u>ember</u> perhaps caused the fire. _____
   A. yellow rock   C. red rock
      found on a beach
   B. piece of glowing   D. fountain
      wood or coal

4. The firefighters fought the blaze <u>aggressively</u> and bravely. _____
   A. from the air   C. in great fear
   B. forcefully   D. with axes and knives

5. The fire <u>consumed</u> almost all the trees and bushes in the area. _____
   A. blew down   C. protected
   B. held in   D. burned up

6. Some of the trees were <u>charred</u> but not burned completely. _____
   A. burned slightly   C. reduced to ashes
   B. scratched   D. dry

7. Eventually the tops of the trees were <u>ablaze</u>. _____
   A. bright green and in bloom   C. falling to earth
   B. in flames   D. saved from fire

8. After a fire, plant life will soon <u>renew</u> itself. _____
   A. relax   C. bring new life to
   B destroy   D. take away some of

Topic, Main Idea, and Supporting Details Chart

Topic: _____

page 662   **Main Idea**
_____
Supporting Details
_____
_____
_____

page 664   **Main Idea**
_____
Supporting Details
Most animals flee from fires.
_____

page 672   **Main Idea**
Wildfires are good for bugs and animals.
Supporting Details
_____
_____
_____

page 674   **Main Idea**
_____
Supporting Details
_____
Small animals run away or hide.
_____

Name _____

A Fire Gone Wild

Complete each sentence with information from the selection Wildfires.

1. The selection mainly deals with the hot, dry summer of _____.

2. On June 23, a _____ started a fire in Yellowstone National Park.

3. Officials previously had allowed such fires to burn themselves out unless _____.

4. Officials changed their mind when more fires _____.

5. Hundreds of _____ were sent to battle and stop the fires.

6. On August 19, the wind blew _____ a mile away and started new fires.

7. August 20, known as _____, saw an area more than twice the size of Chicago burning.

8. _____, not humans, saved the day and finally ended the fires.

9. Yellowstone could now start the process of _____.

10. New _____ began to appear and thrive in the charred woods.

Name _____

What's the Big Idea?

Read the story. Then complete the chart about the topic, main idea, and supporting details on the following page.

Bye-Bye Beaches?

Along both coasts of America, land is being eroded away by the nonstop crashing of ocean waves. During big storms, especially hurricanes, there are pictures on newscasts and in newspapers showing large chunks of earth falling and sliding into the sea. Houses are seen collapsing into the ocean. It's a frightening sight, yet people continue to build homes on the water's edge.

What should these people do about the problem of erosion? Should they build walls to keep the water away? Should they pile up sand into huge mounds that look like dunes? Should they build their homes up high on stilts?

Of course, a problem is who should pay to help keep the water from damaging the land. Many people who own homes on the water believe that the government should pay since it owns much of the coastline. Others believe it is the homeowners' problem, so they should fix it. Some people even want nothing done, believing the beaches should not have houses on them in the first place. They would be happy if all the houses were washed away.

Whatever side you stand on, our beaches need to be protected before they disappear.

Name _____

What's the Big Idea? continued

Complete the chart below about topic, main idea, and supporting details based on "Bye-Bye Beaches?" from the previous page.

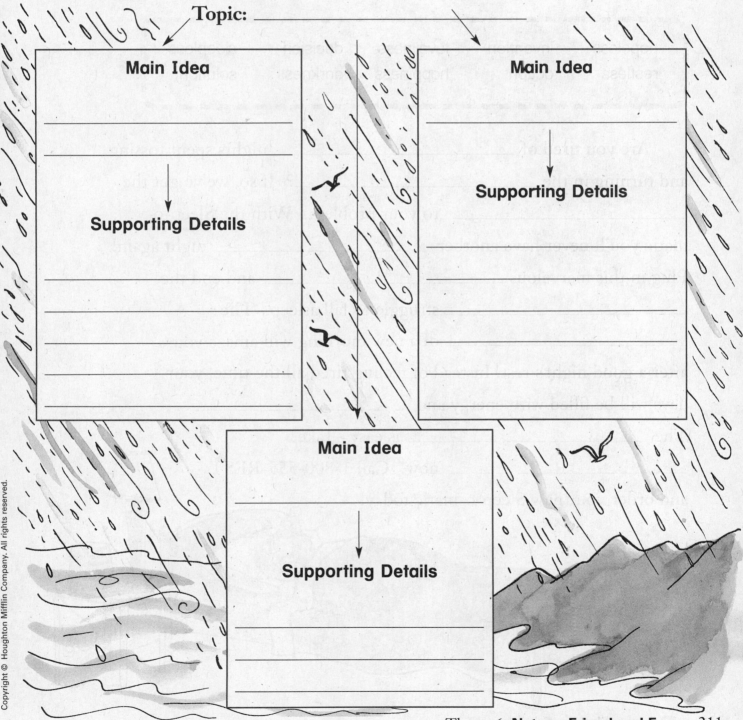

Topic: _____

Main Idea

_____

_____

↓

Supporting Details

_____

_____

_____

_____

Main Idea

_____

↓

Supporting Details

_____

_____

_____

Main Idea

_____

↓

Supporting Details

_____

_____

Name _____

Sleepy Suffixes

**Use what you know about suffixes to help you complete this TV
advertisement with words from the box. If you need help, use a
dictionary.**

hopeless	invention	loveliness	decision	sleepless
restless	action	happiness	darkness	solution

Are you tired of _____ nights spent tossing
and turning in the _____? If so, we've got the
_____ to your problem. With the Sleep-o-
matic you'll never have another _____ night again!
Plug in this marvelous _____ and end the
_____ struggle to fall asleep. The
_____ of a new morning will amaze you
after a good night's rest. Instead of feeling tired all the time, your
days will be filled with energy and _____!
The _____ is easy. Take
_____ now! Call 1-800-555-REST
and order your new Sleep-o-matic today!

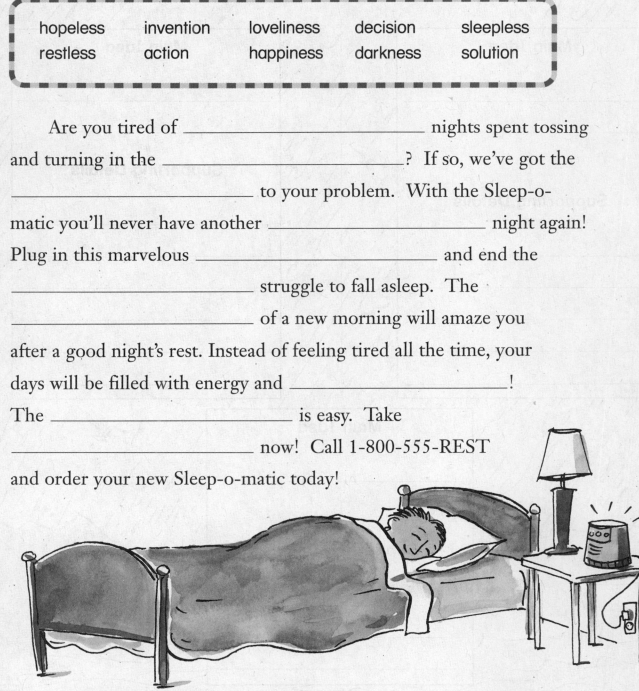

212   Theme 6: **Nature: Friend and Foe**

Name _____

Unusual Spellings

Some words have sounds with unusual spelling patterns.
The spellings of these words have to be remembered.

Write the Spelling Words. Underline the unusual spelling patterns.

Spelling Words

1. health
2. blood
3. type
4. against
5. receive
6. flood
7. month
8. magazine
9. guess
10. women
11. guide
12. style
13. wealth
14. guilt
15. says
16. guard
17. wonder
18. guest
19. gasoline
20. neither

_____ _____

_____ _____

_____ _____

_____ _____

_____ _____

_____ _____

_____ _____

_____ _____

_____ _____

_____ _____

Name _____

Spelling Spree

Sentence Fillers Write the Spelling Word that best completes each sentence.

> **Example**: The naughty puppy chewed my left _____!
>
> *shoe*

1. Be my _____ and help yourself to the food.
2. If you can't find a book, read a _____.
3. The thief admitted his _____.
4. First came the rain, then came the _____.
5. I _____ what I'll be when I grow up.
6. The millionaire accumulated his _____ through hard work.
7. I _____ a letter from my pen pal every month.

1. _____   5. _____

2. _____   6. _____

3. _____   7. _____

4. _____

Words in Words Write the Spelling Word in each word below.

> **Example**: forehead   *head*

8. lifeguard _____

9. bloodshed _____

10. essays _____

11. bimonthly _____

12. guesswork _____

13. typewriter _____

14. freestyle

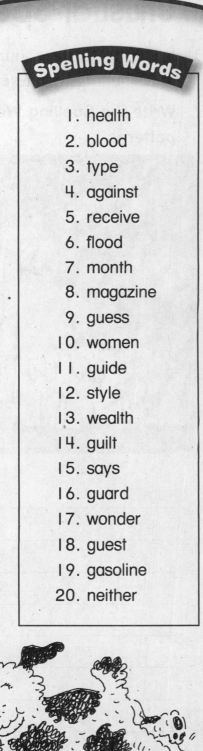

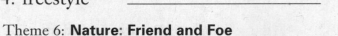

Name _____

Proofreading and Writing

Proofreading Circle the six misspelled Spelling Words in this notice. Then write each word correctly.

State Forestry Service
Warning!

To gard against wildfires, tend your campfires carefully. Put out cooking fires completely, and bury the ashes. Remember, niether matches nor pocket lighters should be used carelessly. Never bring gasaline to a campsite! All men, wemen, and children must follow the rules of safe camping. Your helth and safety depend on it. Pick up our guid on the use of fire in the state forest at the nearest ranger station.

Spelling Words

1. health
2. blood
3. type
4. against
5. receive
6. flood
7. month
8. magazine
9. guess
10. women
11. guide
12. style
13. wealth
14. guilt
15. says
16. guard
17. wonder
18. guest
19. gasoline
20. neither

1. _____   4. _____

2. _____   5. _____

3. _____   6. _____

Write a Safety Poster Everyone must be careful in the woods, for one's own safety and for the protection of the forest. Think of some safety rules or tips for hikers and campers.

On a separate piece of paper, write and decorate a poster about safety in the woods. Use Spelling Words from the list.

Name _____

How Are They Related?

Think about the relationship between the first two items in the analogies below. Write the word that best completes the analogy.

1. **Ankle** is to **wrist** as **knee** is to _____.
   toe   calf   elbow

2. **Right** is to **correct** as **wrong** is to _____.
   grade   incorrect   friend

3. **Seed** is to **sprout** as **child** is to _____.
   grow   play   eat

4. **Ash** is to **burning** as **water** is to _____.
   flame   melting   cold

5. **Pine** is to **tree** as daisy is to _____.
   flower   elm   rose

6. **Writer** is to **poem** as **painter** is to _____.
   paint   sculpture   picture

7. **Softball** is to **sports** as **jazz** is to _____.
   saxophone   music   country

8. **Hard** is to **soft** as **cruel** is to _____.
   friend   enemy   kind

9. **Baby** is to **adult** as **fawn** is to _____.
   deer   lion   pack

10. **Egg** is to **dozen** as **milk** is to _____.
    chocolate   gallon   cow

216   Theme 6: **Nature: Friend and Foe**

Name _____

Writing with Adverbs

Write the correct form of the adverb given in parentheses to complete each statement.

1. After a forest fire, young plants grow

   _____ of all. (quickly)

2. The Yellowstone National Park fire of 1988 burned some areas

   _____ than others. (completely)

3. Animals die in a forest fire _____

   than you might think. (rarely)

4. Some blazes spread _____ than a

   person can run. (fast)

5. Matches are the cause of fires _____

   than some other things. (frequently)

6. The _____ firefighters get to a fire,

   the sooner it can be controlled. (soon)

7. Fire spreads through the treetops

   _____ than it does on the ground.

   (easily)

8. In a fire, energy is released _____ as

   heat and light. (instantly)

9. Fires start from natural causes _____

   than from other causes. (often)

10. Big wildfires burn _____ of all when

    small fires are not allowed to burn. (intensely)

Name _____

Writing with Adverbs

**Write the correct form of the adverb in parentheses to complete
each statement.**

1. After a fire, the owl finds food

   _____ in open areas. (easily)

2. The bison gets to eat new grass

   _____. (often)

3. The woodpecker finds insects _____

   of all in dead bark. (quickly)

4. The tree swallow can build a nest _____

   in a dead tree than in a live one. (rapidly)

5. The deer walks away from a burnout

   _____ than other animals. (soon)

6. The elk finds grass _____ to a fire

   than deer do. (close)

7. The fire beetle lays eggs _____ of all

   in burnt logs. (successfully)

8. The hawk can see food _____ of all

   after a fire. (clearly)

Name _____

Writing with Comparisons

Using *good* and *well* Good writers are careful to use *good* and *well* correctly in their sentences.

Fill in the blanks with either *good* or *well*. Then rewrite each sentence correctly on the line below it.

1. I hope everyone learns the lessons of wildfires _____.
   _____

2. Fire can sometimes be a _____ thing.
   _____

3. Scavengers eat _____ after a fire.
   _____

4. Birds eat many _____ meals of insects.
   _____

5. Rodents find _____ hiding places under rocks.
   _____

6. Other small animals do _____ in burrows.
   _____

7. Some pine cones open only as a result of a _____, hot fire.
   _____

8. It is _____ for them when fire burns away the resin.
   _____

9. Plants without diseases look _____ when checked.
   _____

10. Some of these photos of the fire of 1988 are very _____.
    _____

Name _____

Learning Log Entry

Select three examples of your own writing. Write a paragraph
commenting on your writing. Then fill in the Learning Log entry.

Learning Log

What I Learned:

_____

_____

_____

_____

_____

_____

_____

_____

_____

_____

_____

My Goals:

_____

_____

_____

_____

_____

_____

Name _____

Elaborating with Adverbs

Good writers improve their sentences by using **adverbs**
to tell more. Adverbs can describe verbs, by telling *how* or *when*
an action occurs.

How	When
rapidly	always
quietly	sometimes
quickly	once
noisily	anytime
slowly	now
happily	then
dangerously	again

**Complete the sentences by filling each blank with an adverb
that answers the question in parentheses.**

1. Wet wood burns _____ because
   water keeps air from reaching the fire. (how?)

2. _____, in 1988, fire and smoke in
   Yellowstone Park drove thousands of tourists away. (when?)

3. Gale-force winds can _____ drive
   burning embers to start new fires. (how?)

4. Nature adjusts _____ to changes,
   finding new life in a burnt forest. (how?)

5. New meadows grow _____ where
   once there was scorched earth. (when?)

Name _____

Prairie Scene

Choose the word from the vocabulary list that makes the most sense in the sentence. Write the word on the line provided.

Vocabulary

corral
coyote
drought
phonograph
prairie
slump

1. Among the animals on the Great Plains, the
   _____ dog protects itself by
   burrowing in the ground.

2. When no rain falls for a long time, the land suffers from
   a _____.

3. Sometimes people get so hot in the summer they faint
   and _____ to the ground.

4. Horses on a farm often are kept from wandering by
   enclosing them in a _____.

5. At one time, the only way people could hear music that
   wasn't live was to play records on a
   _____.

6. A _____ is a kind of wolf that
   lives on the prairie.

Name _____

Inferences Chart

Page 690

Details About Anna	_____
	+
What I Know	_____
	=
Inference	_____

Page 692

Details About Papa's Feelings Toward Sarah	_____
	+
What I Know	_____
	=
Inference	_____

Page 700

Details About Sarah and Papa and the Fire	_____
	+
What I Know	_____
	=
Inference	_____

Name _____

The Reasons for Their Actions

Complete the chart below. Fill in the empty boxes to show who does what in *Skylark*, and why. Some boxes have been filled in for you.

Who	What They Do	Why?
page 690: Papa	gets his rifle	to shoot a coyote that is drinking from a bucket at the farm
page 692:	stops Papa from shooting	she feels sorry for the coyote, who only wants water, as the family does
pages 693 – 695: Papa, Anna, and Caleb		because it is her birthday, and they hope it will cheer her up
page 699: Matthew, Maggie, and their children	leave their farm	
page 699:	has a dream about her family playing in lots of water	because she is wishing very hard that the drought will end
page 700: Caleb	runs to get Moonbeam	
page 703: Sarah	shakes her head twice	
page 703:	plans to stay on the farm while the rest of the family goes to Maine	someone needs to take care of the animals and rebuild the farm.

Name _____

Reading Between the Lines

Read the story below. Then answer the questions about the story on the following page.

The Long Wait

Lucy came into the cottage in only her stocking feet. She had left her boots and coat on the porch. She began to warm her hands and feet by the fire when she noticed her brother, Seth, sitting at the kitchen table with a wool blanket wrapped around him, peeling small potatoes for supper.

Seth turned toward Lucy and asked, "How are Starlight and the cows? Did they get enough food?"

"They're doing as well as can be expected," Lucy said. "Starlight's having a bit of trouble breathing again, but she'll be fine."

"You worried about Mama and Pa yet?" Seth asked.

"Nah, not really. They'll be home soon. They only went into town for a few supplies and the wagon ought to be working okay. The snow isn't falling as hard anymore."

"I just hope they will be here soon," Seth said. "I don't like it when our family is apart."

"I know what you mean, Seth. I know what you mean."

Theme 6: **Nature: Friend and Foe**   225

Name _____

Reading Between the Lines continued

Answer the following questions based on your reading of "The Long Wait."

How would you describe Lucy?

Details		What You Know
_____		_____
_____	+	_____
_____		_____
_____		_____
_____		_____

Inference

_____

How would you describe Seth?

Details		What You Know
_____		_____
_____	+	_____
_____		_____
_____		_____
_____		_____

Inference

_____

Name _____

Root Out the Roots

graph means "to write, draw, or record"
tract means "to draw or pull"

**Write the root *graph* or *tract* to complete each word.
Then write the word to complete each sentence.**

1. something that draws attention away:

   dis _____ ion

   The birthday party was a wonderful _____

   from the troubles caused by the drought.

2. pleasing, drawing attention: at _____ ive

   Papa looked _____ in his clean shirt and vest.

3. a written story of a person's life: bio _____ y

   Anna's gift was a _____ about Sarah's life.

4. a division of writing that contains sentences on a single idea:

   para _____

   Sarah read the first _____ aloud.

5. an image recorded by a camera: photo _____

   Anna wished she had a _____ of the party.

**Now write two sentences of your own. In one sentence,
use a word with the root *graph*. In the other, use a word
with the root *tract*.**

_____

_____

_____

_____

Name _____

Silent Consonants

Some words have consonants that are not pronounced. These consonants are called "silent" consonants. The spellings of words with silent consonants have to be remembered.

kneel   clim**b**   cal**f**   **w**rinkle   **h**onest

Write each Spelling Word under the heading that shows its silent consonant.

1. knight
2. soften
3. honor
4. kneel
5. climb
6. wrinkle
7. limb
8. handsome
9. answer
10. calf
11. listen
12. calm
13. knit
14. often
15. palm
16. thumb
17. wrist
18. lamb
19. knob
20. honest

/n/ Spelled *kn*

_____

_____

_____

_____

/r/ Spelled *wr*

_____

_____

/ŏ/ Spelled *ho*

_____

_____

/m/ Spelled *mb*

_____

_____

_____

_____

Silent *l*

_____

_____

Silent *t*

_____

_____

Silent *d*

_____

Silent *w*

_____

Name _____

Spelling Spree

Opposites Write a Spelling Word that means the opposite of each word or group of words below.

Example: right *wrong*

1. question   _____
2. excited   _____
3. harden   _____
4. rarely   _____
5. descend   _____
6. back of the hand _____
7. ugly   _____

Spelling Words

1. knight
2. soften
3. honor
4. kneel
5. climb
6. wrinkle
7. limb
8. handsome
9. answer
10. calf
11. listen
12. calm
13. knit
14. often
15. palm
16. thumb
17. wrist
18. lamb
19. knob
20. honest

Word Addition Write a Spelling Word by adding the beginning of the first word to the middle and end of the second word.

Example: top + walk *talk*

8. know + slob
9. hope + finest
10. write + twinkle
11. knee + light
12. they + crumb
13. wrap + mist
14. list + comb
15. knot + wheel

8. _____   12. _____
9. _____   13. _____
10. _____   14. _____
11. _____   15. _____

Name _____

Proofreading and Writing

Proofreading Circle the five misspelled Spelling Words in this journal entry. Then write each word correctly.

May 9 — I love to lisen to the birds at dawn. Their songs are so happy. They make me hopeful that rain is on the way. As I lay in bed I thought about the new caff born last night. It's strong like its mother. I have the honer of owning not one but three baby animals! This spring a tiny lame was born to my sheep, and Star's colt gets friskier every day. He will be a handsome horse. I have to go now. Before I do my chores, Mother wants me to help her nit a sweater for our friend's baby.

1. knight
2. soften
3. honor
4. kneel
5. climb
6. wrinkle
7. limb
8. handsome
9. answer
10. calf
11. listen
12. calm
13. knit
14. often
15. palm
16. thumb
17. wrist
18. lamb
19. knob
20. honest

1. _____
2. _____
3. _____
4. _____
5. _____

✏ **Write a Weather Report** Prairie families were dependent on the weather for their livelihood. Too little rain would cause the crops to die, but too much rain could result in flash floods. Blizzards and tornadoes were also common on the prairies.

On a separate sheet of paper, write a weather report for a family living on the prairie in the 1800s. Be sure to include details that you think would be useful for a family back then to know. Use Spelling Words from the list.

Name _____

Nouns, Verbs, and Adjectives

**Use each word below in a sentence. Make sure to
use the word as the part of speech given.**

1. stream (v.) _____

_____

2. post (v.) _____

_____

3. post (n.) _____

_____

4. catch (n.) _____

_____

5. fire (v.) _____

_____

**Read the sentences below. Tell the part of speech for the
underlined word.**

6. Sarah walked to the <u>window</u> to look out too. _____

7. Caleb's hair was brushed <u>smooth</u>. _____

8. We will <u>write</u> letters. _____

9. Sometimes it was hard to <u>adapt</u> to prairie life. _____

10. A thin <u>coyote</u> was drinking water out of the pail. _____

Prepositions and Prepositional Phrases

Complete these directions to the farm by using prepositions from the list. You will use some words more than once.

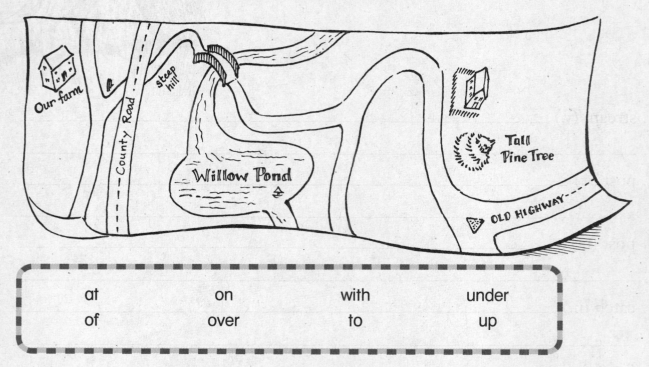

at	on	with	under
of	over	to	up

When you get _____ the Old Highway, turn right.

Soon you will see _____ your right a tree we call the Tall

Pine Tree. Next, you will see a house _____ a picket

fence. Then drive carefully _____ the curvy road until

you turn right again. When the road straightens, you will have a

lovely view _____ Willow Pond. The road turns right and

passes _____ a bridge and _____ a steep hill.

Next you will drive _____ the County Road. Turn right

immediately _____ the stop sign, and you will be

_____ our farm.

Name _____

Completing with Prepositions

**Read the sentences. Underline the prepositions in each
sentence. Then list each prepositional phrase on the lines
provided under each sentence.**

1. The horse paddock is across the driveway from the barn.

   _____

2. The chicken coop is near the vegetable garden.

   _____

3. The farmhouse is at the end of the driveway.

   _____

4. The barn is between the farmhouse and the horse paddock.

   _____

5. The vegetable garden is beside the farmhouse.

   _____

Name _____

Using Prepositions

Good writers use prepositional phrases to add specific
details to their writing.

**Read the paragraph below. Then rewrite it, adding
prepositional phrases to the sentences on the lines
provided. Use phrases from the list.**

> on the phonograph   on the porch
> to the music   out her window
> down the stairs   to her
> in the yard   with a cloth
> of food and drinks

    Wagons were pulling up _____. Sarah

heard the noise outside and looked _____.

Papa saw her running _____. A table

had been set _____. It was full

_____. Papa carried a large object

covered _____. Sarah appeared

_____. Everyone turned

_____ and sang "Happy Birthday."

Papa uncovered the large object. It was a phonograph!

Then Anna handed Papa a record. He put a needle

_____, and soon everyone was

dancing _____.

Name _____

Planning a Speech

Use this graphic organizer to help you plan your speech.
Write notes for a speech about something that happened
to you or something you feel strongly about. Then write
your speech on another sheet of paper.

Title: _____

Opening sentence: _____

_____

Event 1: _____

  details: _____

_____

_____

Event 2: _____

  details: _____

_____

_____

Event 3: _____

  details: _____

_____

_____

_____

Concluding sentence: _____

Name _____

Prepositional Phrases

Good writers combine sentences to make their writing smoother. Sometimes combining sentences with prepositions helps avoid repetition.

Two sentences: Papa looked **up the stairs.**
Papa looked **at Sarah.**
One sentence: Papa looked **up the stairs at Sarah.**
Two sentences: Maggie liked the pink roses.
The roses were **on the dress.**
One sentence: Maggie liked the pink roses **on the dress.**

Combine each set of sentences. You may need to add, delete, or change words to combine the sentences.

1. Sarah and Papa danced. They danced on the lawn.

   _____

2. They could not live without water. The water was in the well.

   _____

3. Anna fell asleep. The time was about midnight.

   _____

4. Sarah wiped the tears. The tears were from her eyes.

   _____

5. The party was a great success. The party was for Sarah's birthday.

   _____

Name _____

Mountain Crossword

Write the vocabulary word that matches each clue in the puzzle. Then answer the question below.

Vocabulary

brush
course
fix
frantic
landslides
sleet
stunned

Across

4. the opposite of *calm*
6. taken by surprise
7. not quite rain and not quite snow

Down

1. falling rocks
2. low bushes
3. if you're in trouble, you're in a
5. path you are taking

8. In the wilderness, why is it important not to become frantic if you find you are off course?

_____

_____

_____

Name _____

Nature: Friend or Foe Chart

Fill in the chart as you read the stories.

How does each character feel about nature in the selection?
Details about Nature in *Lost on a Mountain in Maine*:
_____
_____
What I Know:
_____
_____
My Inference:
_____
_____
Details about Nature in *The Volcano Disaster*:
_____
_____
What I Know:
_____
_____
My Inference:
_____
_____

Inference Chart

Fill in the chart to make inferences about the narrators who tell
the stories of *Lost on a Mountain in Maine* and *Skylark*.

Story and Narrator	What the Narrator Says	What I Know	My Inference about a Character
Donn narrates *Lost on a Mountain in Maine*.	Page 708C: "Guides have said no one could crawl under it, but I did — for a long way." Page 708F: "Sometimes, not knowing the worst helps a fellow along."		
Anna narrates *Skylark*.	Page 692: "I knew that nothing was all right. The look in his eyes was fear." Page 690: "Sarah looked up. 'Yes,' she said. She reached out and touched my hair."		

Volcano Do's and Don'ts

Write the correct word on each line.

Vocabulary

ash
awestruck
cinders
debris
erupt
react
ridge

1. If you see a volcano suddenly _____, follow these directions.

2. **Don't** just stand there _____ by the amazing sight.

3. **Do** _____ to the situation as quickly as possible.

4. **Do** run uphill to a _____ if lava is flowing through a valley.

5. **Don't** trip over fallen trees and other _____ in your path.

6. **Do** wrap a scarf or shirt over your nose and mouth to keep from breathing in powdery _____.

7. **Don't** pick up burning _____ with your bare hands.

Use two Key Vocabulary words to write a sentence about a volcano.

_____

_____

_____

Name _____

Test Practice

Use the three steps you've learned to write a response to the prompt below. Complete the chart, and then write the essay on the lines below it and on page 242. Use the Revising Checklist on page 242 to revise your essay.

Write an essay for your teacher explaining why it is important to thank people for gifts. Include reasons and details.

Opinion		
Reasons	**Reasons**	**Reasons**
Details	**Details**	**Details**

_____

_____

_____

_____

_____

_____

Continue on page 242.

Theme 6: **Nature: Friend and Foe**   241

Name _____

Test Practice continued

_____

_____

_____

_____

_____

_____

_____

_____

_____

_____

_____

_____

Use another piece of paper if you need to.

Revising Checklist

✔ Did I state my opinion clearly in the introduction?

✔ Did I write at least three reasons?

✔ Did I write enough details to support each reason?

✔ Did I write a separate paragraph for each reason?

✔ Did I use exact words? Where can I add more exact words?

✔ Did I use clear handwriting and correct any mistakes?

Read your essay aloud to a partner. Then discuss your answers to the questions on the Revising Checklist. Make any other changes that you think are necessary.

Name _____

How to Plant Daffodils

Read the passage. Then answer the questions.

My aunt Lulu grows the most beautiful flowers. Every spring and summer her front steps are lined with clouds of color. This year Aunt Lulu said I could help her plant daffodils—my favorite.

Lulu had told me to bring over some small rocks, so I did. First we put the rocks in the bottom of the plant pots, and then we filled the pots halfway with soil. Lulu said that the rocks help the water drain. Next, I set three daffodil bulbs in each pot, poured soil over them, and patted it down. We watered each pot and put all the pots in the sun.

Aunt Lulu said I could come over and help her water the bulbs. I can't wait until they bloom!

1. What materials are needed to plant daffodils?

_____

_____

_____

2. List the steps for planting daffodils, in order.

_____

_____

_____

3. What questions might you need to ask to clarify these directions?

_____

_____

_____

Monitoring Student Progress

Comprehension Topic, Main Ideas, and Supporting Details

Name ______________________________

Lost!

Read this passage about Donn Fendler's experience on Mount Katahdin. Then complete the chart below.

Donn Fendler was lost for nine days on Mount Katahdin. The first day of being lost was very difficult for him. Stinging sleet and a bitter wind made him cold and miserable. When he left the trail, a thorny plant called pucker bush often blocked his way. Donn had to crawl under it, cutting his arms and face in the process. The trail, too, was difficult. The rocks were sharp and loose, making each step very dangerous. To make matters worse, Donn became frightened when he passed the same trail sign twice and realized that he had been running in a circle.

Topic	Main Idea	Details

Name _____

Suffixes and Meaning

Read each sentence. Write the base word and the suffix that form each underlined word. Then write the meaning of the underlined word.

1. The night sky was cloudless.

   _____

2. The brightness of the moon allowed Kendra to see the path.

   _____

3. The air was colder at this high elevation.

   _____

4. The stiffness in her leg was getting worse.

   _____

5. She wished she hadn't been so careless when planning the hike.

   _____

6. Kendra refused to feel hopeless.

   _____

7. She pushed away all feelings of desperation.

   _____

8. When the ranger arrived, Kendra felt great happiness.

   _____

Name _____

Choose the Meaning

Read the dictionary entries. Then read each sentence. Write the numbered entry word and the numbered definition that match the underlined word.

> **fair**¹ *adj*. **1.** Beautiful; lovely. **2.** Light in color. **3.** Clear and sunny.
> **4.** Unblemished; clean. **5.** Promising. **6.** Just. **7.** Permissible.
> **8.** Average.
>
> **fair**² *n*. **1.** A market. **2.** An exhibition, as of farm products or crafts.
> **3.** A fund-raising event.

1. Jayden won a blue ribbon at the county <u>fair</u> for her wood carving.

_____

2. The child's hair was curly and <u>fair</u>.

_____

3. He was only a <u>fair</u> baseball player.

_____

4. Our school made money from the book <u>fair</u>.

_____

5. It isn't <u>fair</u> that we have to stay after school.

_____

6. We hope the weather will be <u>fair</u> for the parade.

_____

Name _____

Spelling Review

**Write Spelling Words from the list on this page to
answer the questions.**

1–11. Which eleven words have three syllables?

1. _____   7. _____

2. _____   8. _____

3. _____   9. _____

4. _____   10. _____

5. _____   11. _____

6. _____

12–21. Which ten words have silent consonants?

12. _____   17. _____

13. _____   18. _____

14. _____   19. _____

15. _____   20. _____

16. _____   21. _____

22–30. Which nine remaining words have an unusual
spelling of a short or long vowel sound or the
consonant sound /g/?

22. _____   27. _____

23. _____   28. _____

24. _____   29. _____

25. _____   30. _____

26. _____

Spelling Words

1. listen
2. favorite
3. style
4. library
5. honor
6. deliver
7. knight
8. gasoline
9. alphabet
10. calf
11. however
12. climb
13. handsome
14. another
15. women
16. guard
17. banana
18. neither
19. kneel
20. soften
21. against
22. says
23. remember
24. blood
25. thumb
26. wrist
27. camera
28. health
29. animal
30. wonder

Name _____

Spelling Spree

Analogies Write a Spelling Word that completes each analogy.

1. **Dog** is to **puppy** as **cow** is to _____.

2. **Taste** is to **apple** as _____ is to **music**.

3. **Stand** is to **feet** as _____ is to **knees**.

4. **Electricity** is to **refrigerator** as _____ is to **automobile**.

5. **Pump** is to **water** as **heart** is to _____.

6. **Go** is to **come** as **forget** is to _____.

7. **Heard** is to **hears** as **said** is to

   _____.

8. **Wade** is to **stream** as _____ is to **mountain**.

Phrase Filler Complete each phrase by writing a Spelling Word.

9. a furry little _____

10. my _____ color

11. to _____ why

12. an attractive hair _____

13. a _____ full of books

14. a _____ and film

15. _____ day of rain

Name _____

Proofreading and Writing

Proofreading Circle the six misspelled Spelling Words
in this scientist's log. Then write each word correctly.

*September 12 Today Julia fell, sprained her rist, and hurt
her thum. Then we saw three monkeys share a bannana.
Nature can be both friend and foe. At night one of us is
always on gard. When I keep watch, I lean agianst a tree.
Luckily, niether wild nor tame beasts have bothered us.*

1. honor
2. deliver
3. knight
4. alphabet
5. however
6. handsome
7. women
8. guard
9. banana
10. neither
11. soften
12. against
13. thumb
14. wrist
15. health

1. _____   4. _____

2. _____   5. _____

3. _____   6. _____

Help the Announcer Write Spelling Words in the blanks
to complete this TV commercial.

 Attention men and 7. _____! Do us the 8. _____ of
watching *Nature Knows*. See a wild and 9. _____ lion play
and a huge elephant eat. Watch a baboon 10. _____ a gift to his
girlfriend. Study an entire 11. _____ of animals from ape to zebra.
Seeing cuddly tiger cubs will 12. _____ your views about fierce cats.
All animals are important; 13. _____, many are in trouble. Their
14. _____ is endangered. Be a 15. _____ in shining armor and help
save these animals. Watch our show to find out how.

7. _____   10. _____   13. _____

8. _____   11. _____   14. _____

9. _____   12. _____   15. _____

✏ **Write a Description** On a separate sheet of paper, describe a scientific
trip you would like to take. Use Spelling Review Words.

Name _____

Finding Adverbs

Circle the adverb or adverbs in each sentence. Then write each one in the proper column in the chart below.

1. The hiker walked carefully.

2. Hail was falling everywhere.

3. A frigid wind blew strongly.

4. No shelter could be found nearby.

5. The Saddle Trail led somewhere.

6. Eventually the hiker went quickly in a different direction.

7. He slowly crawled through a patch of bushes.

8. Then the sun shone brightly for a moment.

9. The hiker glanced downward.

10. He looked happily at a lake.

How	Where	When
_____	_____	_____
_____	_____	_____
_____	_____	_____
_____	_____	
_____		

Name _____

Finding Prepositions and Prepositional Phrases

Underline the preposition in each sentence. Then list the prepositional phrase on the line below the sentence.

1. The boy ran down the trail.

   _____

2. He looked at his watch.

   _____

3. The volcano would erupt at any moment.

   _____

4. He stopped for a rest.

   _____

5. Suddenly the ground under his feet fell away.

   _____

6. A loud noise echoed in the forest.

   _____

7. The boy scrambled to his feet and ran.

   _____

8. Steam rose from the volcano.

   _____

Student Handbook

Contents

How to Study a Word

I. LOOK at the word.
► What does the word mean?
► What letters are in the word?
► Name and touch each letter.

2. SAY the word.
► Listen for the consonant sounds.
► Listen for the vowel sounds.

3. THINK about the word.
► How is each sound spelled?
► Close your eyes and picture the word.
► What familiar spelling patterns do you see?
► Did you see any prefixes, suffixes, or other word parts?

4. WRITE the word.
► Think about the sounds and the letters.
► Form the letters correctly.

5. CHECK the spelling.
► Did you spell the word the same way it is spelled in your word list?
► If you did not spell the word correctly, write the word again.

again	eighth	January		
all right	enough			
a lot	every	knew		
also	everybody	know	really	two
always	everyone		received	tying
another	excite	let's	right	
anyone		letter		until
anything	family	little	said	usually
anyway	favorite	loose	Saturday	
around	February	lose	school	very
	finally	lying	someone	
beautiful	first		stopped	weird
because	friend	might	stretch	we're
before		millimeter	suppose	where
believe	getting	minute	sure	while
brought	girl	morning	swimming	whole
build	goes	myself		won't
buy	going		than	world
	guess	ninety	that's	would
cannot			their	wouldn't
can't	happened	o'clock	then	write
caught	haven't	off	there	writing
choose	heard	once	there's	
chose	height	other	they	your
clothes	here	our	they're	you're
coming			thought	
could	I'd	people	through	
cousin	I'll	pretty	to	
	I'm	probably	tongue	
didn't	instead		tonight	
different	into	quit	too	
divide	its	quite	tried	
don't	it's		truly	

Problem Solvers
Reading-Writing
Workshop

Look for familiar spelling patterns in these words to help you remember their spellings.

My Name Is
María Isabel

The /k/, /ng/, and /kw/ Sounds

/k/	→	shark, attack, public
/ng/	→	sink
/kw/	→	question

Spelling Words

1. sure
2. here
3. knew
4. might
5. pretty
6. really
7. very
8. where
9. little
10. until
11. into
12. off
13. said
14. our
15. letter

Spelling Words

1. shark
2. attack
3. risk
4. public
5. sink
6. question
7. electric
8. jacket
9. blank
10. ache
11. crooked
12. drink
13. topic
14. track
15. blanket
16. struck
17. mistake
18. junk
19. squirrel
20. stomach

Challenge Words

1. finally
2. different
3. excite
4. truly
5. suppose

Challenge Words

1. aquatic
2. comic
3. tropical
4. speckled
5. peculiar

My Study List
Add your own
spelling words
on the back. ➡

My Study List
Add your own
spelling words
on the back. ➡

Name _____

My Study List

1. _____
2. _____
3. _____
4. _____
5. _____
6. _____
7. _____
8. _____
9. _____
10. _____

Review Words

1. quick
2. luck
3. picnic
4. basket
5. sock

How to Study a Word

Look at the word.
Say the word.
Think about the word.
Write the word.
Check the spelling.

Take-Home Word List

Name _____

My Study List

1. _____
2. _____
3. _____
4. _____
5. _____
6. _____
7. _____
8. _____
9. _____
10. _____

How to Study a Word

Look at the word.
Say the word.
Think about the word.
Write the word.
Check the spelling.

258

The Last Dragon

Final /j/ and /s/
/j/ ➡ bri**dge**, stran**ge**
/ĭj/ ➡ villa**ge**
/s/ ➡ fen**ce**

Spelling Words

1. village	11. glance
2. cottage	12. ridge
3. bridge	13. manage
4. fence	14. damage
5. strange	15. since
6. chance	16. marriage
7. twice	17. edge
8. cage	18. lodge
9. change	19. cabbage
10. carriage	20. dodge

Challenge Words

1. fleece
2. fragrance
3. homage
4. fringe
5. excellence

My Study List
Add your own
spelling words
on the back. ➡

Marven of the Great North Woods

Final /ē/
Final /ē/ ➡ beaut**y**, hon**ey**

Spelling Words

1. beauty	11. duty
2. ugly	12. hungry
3. lazy	13. lonely
4. marry	14. alley
5. ready	15. body
6. sorry	16. twenty
7. empty	17. turkey
8. honey	18. hockey
9. valley	19. fifty
10. movie	20. monkey

Challenge Words

1. fiery
2. envy
3. mercy
4. chimney
5. imaginary

My Study List
Add your own
spelling words
on the back. ➡

Name _____

My Study List

1. _____
2. _____
3. _____
4. _____
5. _____
6. _____
7. _____
8. _____
9. _____
10. _____

Review Words

1. pretty
2. sadly
3. friendly
4. city
5. slowly

How to Study a Word

Look at the word.
Say the word.
Think about the word.
Write the word.
Check the spelling.

260

Name _____

My Study List

1. _____
2. _____
3. _____
4. _____
5. _____
6. _____
7. _____
8. _____
9. _____
10. _____

Review Words

1. nice
2. place
3. huge
4. judge
5. page

How to Study a Word

Look at the word.
Say the word.
Think about the word.
Write the word.
Check the spelling.

260

Happy Birthday, Dr. King!

Words with a Prefix or a Suffix

re + paint = **re**paint
dis + like = **dis**like
un + lucky = **un**lucky
un + pack = **un**pack
sick**ness**   treat**ment**
beauti**ful**   care**less**

Spelling Words

1. redo
2. treatment
3. rebuild
4. discolor
5. careless
6. dislike
7. sickness
8. beautiful
9. unlucky
10. awful
11. reread
12. unsure
13. movement
14. peaceful
15. unpaid
16. distrust
17. kindness
18. useless
19. displease
20. powerful

Challenge Words

1. unusual
2. rearrange
3. appointment
4. discontinue
5. resourceful

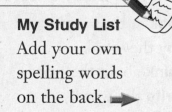

My Study List
Add your own spelling words on the back. ➡

Problem Solvers
Spelling Review

Spelling Words

1. sink
2. squirrel
3. question
4. twenty
5. alley
6. twice
7. chance
8. glance
9. thirty
10. afraid
11. blanket
12. crooked
13. honey
14. monkey
15. ready
16. cottage
17. since
18. other
19. corner
20. office
21. mistake
22. attack
23. lonely
24. beauty
25. strange
26. ridge
27. village
28. suppose
29. degree
30. whether

See the back for Challenge Words.

My Study List
Add your own spelling words on the back. ➡

Sing to the Stars

VCCV Pattern
VC | CV :   **dan|ger,**
            at|tend,
            din|ner
V | CCV :   **a|fraid**
VCC | V :   **rock|et**

Spelling Words

1. bottom
2. picture
3. other
4. attend
5. capture
6. common
7. danger
8. afraid
9. borrow
10. office
11. arrow
12. suppose
13. escape
14. whether
15. pillow
16. dinner
17. thirty
18. degree
19. allow
20. corner

Challenge Words

1. method
2. concert
3. narrate
4. abrupt
5. challenge

My Study List
Add your own spelling words on the back. ➡

Name _____

My Study List

1. _____
2. _____
3. _____
4. _____
5. _____
6. _____
7. _____
8. _____
9. _____
10. _____

Review Words

1. between
2. lesson
3. enjoy
4. happen
5. teacher

How to Study a Word

Look at the word.
Say the word.
Think about the word.
Write the word.
Check the spelling.

Name _____

My Study List

1. _____
2. _____
3. _____
4. _____
5. _____
6. _____
7. _____
8. _____
9. _____
10. _____

Challenge Words

1. comic   6. tropical
2. aquatic   7. chimney
3. imaginary   8. fiery
4. homage   9. fleece
5. concert   10. narrate

How to Study a Word

Look at the word.
Say the word.
Think about the word.
Write the word.
Check the spelling.

Name _____

My Study List

1. _____
2. _____
3. _____
4. _____
5. _____
6. _____
7. _____
8. _____
9. _____
10. _____

Review Words

1. hopeful
2. remake
3. rewrite
4. useful
5. unfair

How to Study a Word

Look at the word.
Say the word.
Think about the word.
Write the word.
Check the spelling.

Lou Gehrig

VCV Pattern

V | CV :   pi | lot,
              mo | ment
VC | V :   vis | it,
              par | ent

Spelling Words

1. pilot
2. depend
3. visit
4. human
5. seven
6. chosen
7. paper
8. reason
9. become
10. parent
11. never
12. modern
13. tiny
14. tuna
15. event
16. fever
17. moment
18. prison
19. basic
20. open

Challenge Words

1. alert
2. license
3. select
4. radar
5. feature

My Study List
Add your own
spelling words
on the back. ➡

263

Gloria Estefan

Changing Final *y* to *i*

city   + es   = cit**ies**
study   + ed   = stud**ied**
sunny   + er   = sunn**ier**
heavy   + est = heav**iest**

Spelling Words

1. sunnier
2. cloudier
3. windier
4. cities
5. heaviest
6. prettiest
7. studied
8. easier
9. noisier
10. families
11. ferries
12. crazier
13. funnier
14. earlier
15. copied
16. hobbies
17. angriest
18. emptied
19. worried
20. happiest

Challenge Words

1. iciest
2. hazier
3. breezier
4. companies
5. qualities

My Study List
Add your own
spelling words
on the back. ➡

263

Heroes
Reading-Writing Workshop

Look for familiar spelling patterns in these words to help you remember their spellings.

Spelling Words

1. brought
2. enough
3. buy
4. guess
5. Saturday
6. January
7. February
8. favorite
9. lying
10. tying
11. around
12. swimming
13. heard
14. also
15. tried

Challenge Words

1. choose
2. chose
3. loose
4. lose
5. millimeter

My Study List
Add your own
spelling words
on the back. ➡

263

Take-Home Word List

Name _____

📝 My Study List

1. _____
2. _____
3. _____
4. _____
5. _____
6. _____
7. _____
8. _____
9. _____
10. _____

How to Study a Word

Look at the word.
Say the word.
Think about the word.
Write the word.
Check the spelling.

Take-Home Word List

Name _____

📝 My Study List

1. _____
2. _____
3. _____
4. _____
5. _____
6. _____
7. _____
8. _____
9. _____
10. _____

Review Words

1. hurried
2. stories
3. carried
4. pennies
5. babies

How to Study a Word

Look at the word.
Say the word.
Think about the word.
Write the word.
Check the spelling.

Take-Home Word List

Name _____

📝 My Study List

1. _____
2. _____
3. _____
4. _____
5. _____
6. _____
7. _____
8. _____
9. _____
10. _____

Review Words

1. before
2. travel
3. orange
4. ever
5. begin

How to Study a Word

Look at the word.
Say the word.
Think about the word.
Write the word.
Check the spelling.

Nature: Friend and Foe
Reading-Writing Workshop

Look for familiar spelling patterns in these words to help you remember their spellings.

Spelling Words

1. their	9. too
2. there	10. two
3. they're	11. they
4. your	12. than
5. you're	13. then
6. its	14. right
7. it's	15. write
8. to	

Challenge Words

1. all right
2. usually
3. eighth
4. height
5. tongue

My Study List
Add your own spelling words on the back. ➡

265

Take-Home Word List

Salmon Summer

Three-Syllable Words
yes | ter | day ➡
/yĕs′ tər dā/
de | liv | er ➡
/dĭ lĭv′ ər/

Spelling Words

1. deliver	11. enemy
2. favorite	12. animal
3. camera	13. another
4. yesterday	14. however
5. tomorrow	15. banana
6. important	16. alphabet
7. together	17. hospital
8. victory	18. hamburger
9. remember	19. carpenter
10. library	20. several

Challenge Words

1. interview
2. article
3. halibut
4. edition
5. photograph

My Study List
Add your own spelling words on the back. ➡

265

Take-Home Word List

Heroes
Spelling Review

Spelling Words

1. redo	16. worried
2. unsure	17. angriest
3. useless	18. paper
4. kindness	19. parent
5. easier	20. prison
6. copied	21. reread
7. crazier	22. peaceful
8. seven	23. powerful
9. become	24. studied
10. fever	25. earlier
11. dislike	26. happiest
12. movement	27. visit
13. displease	28. reason
14. cities	29. never
15. families	30. tuna

See the back for Challenge Words.

My Study List
Add your own spelling words on the back. ➡

265

Take-Home Word List

Take-Home Word List

Take-Home Word List

Name _____

Name _____

Name _____

My Study List

1. _____
2. _____
3. _____
4. _____
5. _____
6. _____
7. _____
8. _____
9. _____
10. _____

My Study List

1. _____
2. _____
3. _____
4. _____
5. _____
6. _____
7. _____
8. _____
9. _____
10. _____

My Study List

1. _____
2. _____
3. _____
4. _____
5. _____
6. _____
7. _____
8. _____
9. _____
10. _____

Challenge Words

1. unusual
2. resourceful
3. breezer
4. select
5. radar
6. discontinue
7. companies
8. iciest
9. alert
10. license

Review Words

1. grandmother
2. grandfather
3. October
4. November
5. unhappy

How to Study a Word

Look at the word.
Say the word.
Think about the word.
Write the word.
Check the spelling.

How to Study a Word

Look at the word.
Say the word.
Think about the word.
Write the word.
Check the spelling.

How to Study a Word

Look at the word.
Say the word.
Think about the word.
Write the word.
Check the spelling.

Nature: Friend and Foe
Spelling Review

Spelling Words

1. favorite
2. camera
3. banana
4. remember
5. neither
6. against
7. wonder
8. climb
9. thumb
10. calf
11. animal
12. however
13. alphabet
14. health
15. guard
16. blood
17. women
18. listen
19. honor
20. kneel
21. another
22. library
23. deliver
24. says
25. gasoline
26. style
27. soften
28. wrist
29. handsome
30. knight

See the back for Challenge Words.

Skylark

Silent Consonants
Some words have a consonant that is not pronounced.

kneel clim**b** calf
wrinkle **h**onest

Spelling Words

1. knight
2. soften
3. honor
4. kneel
5. climb
6. wrinkle
7. limb
8. handsome
9. answer
10. calf
11. listen
12. calm
13. knit
14. often
15. palm
16. thumb
17. wrist
18. lamb
19. knob
20. honest

Challenge Words
1. drought
2. knoll
3. heir
4. debt
5. wrestle

Wildfires

Unusual Spellings
/ĕ/ → h**ea**lth, ag**ai**nst, s**ay**s
/ĭ/ → w**o**men
/ŭ/ → bl**oo**d, m**o**nth
/ē/ → rec**ei**ve, magaz**i**ne
/ī/ → t**y**pe
/g/ → **gu**ess

Spelling Words

1. health
2. blood
3. type
4. against
5. receive
6. flood
7. month
8. magazine
9. guess
10. women
11. guide
12. style
13. wealth
14. guilt
15. says
16. guard
17. wonder
18. guest
19. gasoline
20. neither

Challenge Words
1. vaccine
2. quarantine
3. guarantee
4. threaten
5. rhyme

My Study List
Add your own spelling words on the back. ➡

My Study List
Add your own spelling words on the back. ➡

My Study List
Add your own spelling words on the back. ➡

Name _____

My Study List

1. _____
2. _____
3. _____
4. _____
5. _____
6. _____
7. _____
8. _____
9. _____
10. _____

Review Words

1. front
2. head
3. does
4. shoe
5. gym

How to Study a Word

Look at the word.
Say the word.
Think about the word.
Write the word.
Check the spelling.

268

Name _____

My Study List

1. _____
2. _____
3. _____
4. _____
5. _____
6. _____
7. _____
8. _____
9. _____
10. _____

Review Words

1. talk
2. knife
3. wrong
4. knock
5. hour

How to Study a Word

Look at the word.
Say the word.
Think about the word.
Write the word.
Check the spelling.

268

Name _____

My Study List

1. _____
2. _____
3. _____
4. _____
5. _____
6. _____
7. _____
8. _____
9. _____
10. _____

Challenge Words

1. halibut
2. photograph
3. rhyme
4. drought
5. debt
6. edition
7. threaten
8. guarantee
9. heir
10. knoll

How to Study a Word

Look at the word.
Say the word.
Think about the word.
Write the word.
Check the spelling.

268

Focus on Pourquoi Tales

More VCV Pattern	
V | CV :	ti|ger
VC | V :	clev|er

Spelling Words

1. tiger
2. belong
3. clever
4. wagon
5. defend
6. river
7. award
8. season
9. metal
10. palace
11. spider
12. frozen
13. figure
14. police
15. dragon
16. exit
17. decide
18. delay
19. finish
20. total

Challenge Words

1. prepare
2. garage
3. peril
4. giraffe
5. rival

My Study List
Add your own
spelling words
on the back. ➡

Focus on Poetry

More VCCV Pattern	
VC | CV :	gar|den
	yel|low
V | CCV :	a|pron
VCC | V :	rath|er

Spelling Words

1. garden
2. yellow
3. rather
4. secret
5. package
6. apron
7. narrow
8. chicken
9. gather
10. declare
11. entire
12. bucket
13. rabbit
14. engine
15. nothing
16. person
17. silver
18. number
19. rocket
20. limber

Challenge Words

1. publish
2. rascal
3. reflect
4. vibrate
5. disturb

My Study List
Add your own
spelling words
on the back. ➡

Take-Home Word List

Name _____

My Study List

1. _____
2. _____
3. _____
4. _____
5. _____
6. _____
7. _____
8. _____
9. _____
10. _____

Review Words

1. follow
2. party
3. hello
4. market
5. balloon

How to Study a Word

Look at the word.
Say the word.
Think about the word.
Write the word.
Check the spelling.

Take-Home Word List

Name _____

My Study List

1. _____
2. _____
3. _____
4. _____
5. _____
6. _____
7. _____
8. _____
9. _____
10. _____

Review Words

1. water
2. color
3. today
4. ahead
5. alive

How to Study a Word

Look at the word.
Say the word.
Think about the word.
Write the word.
Check the spelling.

Problem Words

Words	Rules	Examples
are our	*Are* is a verb. *Our* is a possessive pronoun.	<u>Are</u> these gloves yours? This is <u>our</u> car.
doesn't don't	Use *doesn't* with singular nouns, *he*, *she*, and *it*. Use *don't* with plural nouns, *I*, *you*, *we*, and *they*.	Dad <u>doesn't</u> swim. We <u>don't</u> swim.
good well	Use the adjective *good* to describe nouns. Use the adverb *well* to describe verbs.	The weather looks <u>good</u>. She sings <u>well</u>.
its it's	*Its* is a possessive pronoun. *It's* is a contraction of *it is*.	The dog wagged <u>its</u> tail. <u>It's</u> cold today.
set sit	*Set* means "to put." *Sit* means "to rest or stay in one place."	<u>Set</u> the vase on the table. Please <u>sit</u> in this chair.
their there they're	*Their* means "belonging to them." *There* means "at or in that place." *They're* is a contraction of *they are*.	<u>Their</u> coats are on the bed. Is Carlos <u>there</u>? <u>They're</u> going to the store.
two to too	*Two* is a number *To* means "toward." *Too* means "also" or "more than enough."	I bought <u>two</u> shirts. A cat ran <u>to</u> the tree. Can we go <u>too</u>? I ate <u>too</u> many peas.
your you're	*Your* is a possessive pronoun. *You're* is a contraction of *you are*.	Are these <u>your</u> glasses? <u>You're</u> late again!

Read each question below. Then check your paper. Correct any mistakes you find. After you have corrected them, put a check mark in the box next to the question.

☐   1. Did I indent each paragraph?

☐   2. Does each sentence tell one complete thought?

☐   3. Do I have any run-on sentences?

☐   4. Did I spell all words correctly?

☐   5. Did I use capital letters correctly?

☐   6. Did I use punctuation marks correctly?

☐   7. Did I use commas and apostrophes correctly?

☐   8. Did I spell all the words the right way?

Is there anything else you should look for? Make your own proofreading checklist.

☐ _____

☐ _____

☐ _____

☐ _____

☐ _____

☐ _____

☐ _____

Mark	Explanation	Examples
¶	Begin a new paragraph. Indent the paragraph.	¶The boat finally arrived. It was two hours late.
∧	Add letters, words, or sentences.	My ^best^ friend ate lunch with me t^o^day.
◌	Take out words, sentences, and punctuation marks. Correct spelling.	We ~~looked at and~~ admired, the mod~~d~~el airplanes.
≡	Change a small letter to a capital letter.	New York c̲i̲t̲y̲ is exciting.
/	Change a capital letter to a small letter.	The /Fireflies blinked in the dark.
⌄⌄	Add quotation marks.	⌄Where do you want the piano?⌄ asked the movers.
∧	Add a comma.	Carlton ∧ my cat ∧ has a mind of his own.
⊙	Add a period.	Put a period at the end of the sentence⊙
∼	Reverse letters or words.	Raed carefully the instructions.
?	Add a question mark.	Should I put the mark here?
!	Add an exclamation mark.	Look out below!